Bush & Mountain Flying

3rd Edition
July 2017

Advanced flying techniques
and procedures
for the backcountry

"CC" Milne Pocock

COPYRIGHT

3rd edition published in the United States of America, July 2017.
© "CC" Milne Pocock.
ISBN 978-1-942634-67-6

2nd edition published in South Africa 2013.
Revised and published in the USA 2014.
4 revisions in total. 4th revision December 2015
Published as an E-book December 2015
© "CC" Milne Pocock.
ISBN 978-0-620-49666-7

1st edition published in South Africa 2009
© "CC" Milne Pocock.
ISBN 978-0-620-43534-5

Author's Contact Details
Email: info@bush-air.com
Website URLs: bush-air.com bushair.co

The Discovery Channel logo is a trademark of Discovery Channel and Discovery Communications, Inc. and its use does not imply any affiliation or endorsement of any content or procedures contained herein.

ACKNOWLEDGEMENTS

Photographs: Gary Kegal, Markus Möllmann, Wayne Calitz, Frank Henning & Kat Tiefenthal.

Cover photo of 3rd edition: Gary Kegal

Cover photo of 2nd edition: Frank Henning.

Cover photo of 1st edition: Markus Möllmann.

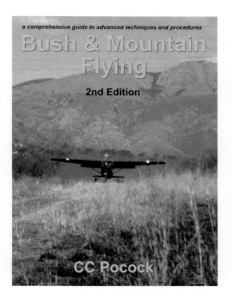

1st edition 2009   2nd edition 2014

Contents

Part 4. Electrical and avionics, fault diagnostics and repairs 251

AUTHOR'S INTRODUCTION

I was fascinated with flying since a very young age and since even before the start of my official flight training I already had an interest in bush flying. Before I even had my private checkride, I was already buzzing tree tops during my solo flights. Being signed out by an instructor to go solo in the general flight training area was a good excuse to do all kinds of exciting stuff, like touch & go's on farm fields and roads.

In the beginning my main source of income was producing laser, special effects and fireworks displays. After obtaining a commercial license, I was already flying into unprepared off-airport areas and occasionally coaching pilots in basic bush flying skills. Much later on, I started bush flying courses with simple ring bound notes and Bush Air was born.

I started performing at airshows and fly-ins, demonstrating the capabilities of general aviation light aircraft, particularly the 172, as it is the world's most popular training aircraft and the most successful mass-produced light aircraft in history. In 1999, I had the opportunity to pioneer and introduce the use of pyrotechnics at an airshow in South Africa for the first time, fusing together my two specialties.

During the early years, prior to my advanced flying courses and Bush Air, I was involved in a few aircraft accidents and incidents during my various escapades, all due to my own pilot error. I acquired many advanced flying skills the hard way over many years and I am very lucky and grateful to have survived some very severe accidents. My experiences led to my sole objective being to pass these skills and techniques on to pilots who not only want to become professional safe bush pilots, but also pilots who just want to become safer, more proficient and confident with their aircraft and the environment that they fly in, without the dangers of having to learn the hard way like I did and possibly not surviving a crash. I realized that there are far too many fatal light aircraft accidents during landings and take-offs from short or hot & high strips and particularly controlled flight into terrain (CFIT) in mountainous areas during bad weather, due to lack of experience, poor training and pilot error. All these accidents were totally unnecessary and could have been prevented by proper practical advanced flight training.

In 2000 I started looking for the ideal location to build a home base for Bush Air and Pyro-Fx. In 2002 I sold my private airfield (Laser) north of Johannesburg and purchased 120 acres of land in the Barberton Valley, South Africa. Originally I named it "Bush Air", then after consultation with the Barberton Town Council, my airfield became the official "Barberton Airport" (FABR).

I ran Advanced Bush & Mountain Flying Courses on my airport for 15 successful years. However during all this time the South African Civil Aviation Authority (SACAA) refused to accept or acknowledge my courses were of any value to aviation safety. Instead they tried to shut me down, without any success. In May 2015 the US Federal Aviation Administration (FAA) Safety Team accredited my courses and approved myself and Bush Air as a training provider.

In 2016 I immigrated to the United States.

At the time this edition went to print, nearly 600 pilots consisting of Private, Commercial, Airline Transport, Instructors and Examiners from all over the world have attended my Advanced Flight Training.

ABOUT THIS BOOK

I was originally motivated to write the first edition of this book for two reasons, firstly to protect the copyright of the information contained in my original ring bound course notes and secondly due to the fact that there had never been a comprehensive handbook combining the highly misunderstood and advanced subjects of bush flying, mountain flying, survival and aircraft technical all into one book.

There are other individual books on bush, mountain, float and ski flying available.

Apart from my original ring bound course notes I had never written anything before in my life and never imagined myself ever becoming an author. It has been a major learning curve to say the least, especially as I chose to self publish.

I was very cautious and conservative in the way I wrote the 1st edition as it was the first book of its kind and I was unsure as to how some people would react to it. In the 2nd edition I decided to elaborate a bit more on techniques and procedures that although may be frowned upon by some, definitely produce amazing results. I also covered as much as I could on turbo-prop operations.

This book focuses mainly on highly advanced techniques and skills required to operate safely in remote, challenging and extreme conditions.

However, before reading this book any further, please read the 'Disclaimer and Warning' as most of the flying techniques mentioned in this book are of such an extreme nature that they should never be attempted by any inexperienced, non-proficient or poorly trained pilot.

DISCLAIMER AND SAFETY WARNING

Whilst every care and effort has been taken in compiling the information in this book, the author will not be held responsible for the accuracy of the contents nor any legal action arising from the use thereof.

Some of the information contained in this book is of a highly advanced and extreme nature and intended for use solely as an educational guide. All pilots intending to use any of the techniques mentioned in this book should attend the authors Advanced Bush & Mountain Flying course or at least obtain advanced training or instruction from an instructor suitably qualified and experienced in similar advanced bush and mountain flying techniques.

It is the responsibility of the pilot to ensure that all techniques, procedures, maneuvers, maintenance and repairs explained in this book are fully within his/her capabilities. The use of any information in this book is entirely at his/her own risk. Most techniques in this book cannot be learned by simply reading about them and then experimenting in the air.

The techniques in this book explore the very edge of the airplane's performance envelope and include flying close to stall speeds at low altitudes and thus are extremely dangerous to inexperienced pilots without the required skills and judgement.

It is the responsibility of the pilot in command of an aircraft to ensure that he/she complies with the regulations of the country that he/she is flying in. Any information in this book that may lead to the contravention of any rules, laws or regulations is used entirely at the pilot's own risk. Any person who uses any information in this book accepts full risk and responsibility.

The author of this book shall not be held liable for any loss or damage caused directly or indirectly as a result of using any information, procedures or techniques contained in this book.

TRAINING

Any pilot who is looking for training or mentoring in Bush and Mountain Flying skills and techniques should seek it from an appropriately skilled, experienced and knowledgeable pilot in this field and not a flight instructor whose claim to fame is flying around the "cabbage patch" or only flying charters or airliners. A flight instructor rating does not qualify one as an instant "flight guru", knowledgeable in all aspects of flying, nor does it make one an appropriately skilled, experienced and knowledgeable pilot in bush and mountain flying.

Most flight instructors are themselves relatively low time pilots and inexperienced in general aviation. They only know what they were taught during their private, commercial and instructors training which consisted mainly of basic theory, procedures and flying techniques which they pass onto the student or pilot that they are training. They themselves may never have explored the full envelope of the aircraft that they fly or expanded their own envelope (advanced techniques, skills and knowledge). There are also many flight instructors with thousands of hours who, although have been instructing all their lives, may have never experienced or discovered anything other than the small envelope they have known since they started flying. You may learn a lot more from an experienced and proficient private pilot than from many flight instructors.

What I am trying to emphasize is that you should be very careful when choosing a pilot or instructor that claims to be a professional or experienced "Bush and Mountain Pilot" or a flight school that offers "Bush Pilot Courses". Most so called "Bush Pilot Courses" are nothing more than a gimmick.

DEFINITION OF BUSH FLYING

Most people do not know the real meaning of the terms "Bush Flying" or "Bush Pilot". Many pilots believe that they are "Bush Pilots" merely because they have flown in a "bushy" environment and landed on suitably maintained dirt or grass strips of an acceptable length in a standard airplane. Virtually, any pilot with a fresh private pilot certificate can do that. You may have done some flying in the bush, but you may not necessarily be a Bush Pilot!

"Bush Flying" is a term for aircraft operations carried out in remote, rough and inhospitable regions all over the world. "Bush Flying" involves operations in rough terrain where there are often no prepared landing strips or runways, frequently necessitating that bush planes be equipped with abnormally large tyres, floats or skis.

"Bush Flying" as it is known today originated in the Canadian and Alaskan tundra and eventually further South into the African bush, Australian outback and jungles of South America and Papua New Guinea. Originally started to provide logistics like food, medicine and mail to isolated communities, bush operations grew rapidly to geological, wildlife and reconnaissance expeditions, hunting, climbing and hiking.

"Bush Flying" has attracted many of the world's most famous aviators whose pioneering exploits helped push back the frontiers on some of the most inhospitable parts of the world.

A "Bush Pilot" is a person who is able to fly a light to medium size aircraft safely in and out of places that would normally be regarded by most other pilots as "marginal", "too dangerous" or "impossible". Generally these are areas that are inaccessible to most aircraft and other means of transportation. Furthermore, a "Bush Pilot" should be able to maintain and repair the aircraft and survive in the bush.

A "Bush Pilot" should have a thorough knowledge of the hazards of Bush and Mountain Flying, have a higher than normal level of skill and judgement and be fully competent and proficient in the advanced techniques required to safely fly in these areas. The life and death nature of Bush Flying also means that bush pilots frequently resort to unorthodox and untested methods for accomplishing the job. Many common aviation practices where pioneered in Bush Flying.

"Bush Pilots" must fend for themselves because they are so far from help. Critical skills range from survival to mechanical and electrical skills for airplane repair to hunting, trapping, shelter building and first aid.

"Bush Pilots" need to know how to deal with common engine, airframe, electrical and avionics problems that may occur from time to time, including important maintenance issues. When operating out in remote parts of the bush it may not be possible to get a qualified aircraft mechanic to assist you.

This type of flying, combined with unpredictable weather and distance from help, means that "Bush Pilots" have to be very resourceful to be successful, or all too frequently, just to stay alive: a "Jack of all Trades" - pilot, mechanic, cook, hunter, medic etc. A bush plane needs to be properly equipped for operating in remote and rough areas. Such an aircraft should be fitted with a reliable and powerful engine/s, strong landing gear and high floatation oversize tyres. The pilot should always be ready for any eventuality and carry the necessary basic tools, spares and survival equipment.

Bush and Mountain Flying is a highly specialized and skilled art!

CHAPTER 1

BUSH FLYING

1. Author's Cessna 170-B trainer is equipped with various Supplemental Type Certificates (STC's), including a Sportsman leading edge STOL cuff , aileron gap seals, vortex generators, drooped wing tips, 10" wheels and 31" tires.

2. Author's Cessna 172-C trainer seen here with 8:50x6" main wheels and 6:00x6" nose wheel. Since going to print, the wings have also been modified with a Sportsman leading edge cuff, aileron gap seals and wing tips.

BUSH FLYING

Part 1. Aircraft

High wing or low wing?

There is absolutely no question as to which one is most suitable for bush work. Only a high wing airplane can clear long grass, shrubs, small bushes and trees, debris and low fence lines along roads, also the visibility from a high wing is better. The undercarriage on a high wing is generally far stronger and more flexible than that of a low wing.

The high wing also offers shelter from the elements when on the ground. This also assists loading and unloading in bad weather and if your tent is pitched under the wing, you have easy dry access between the tent and the aircraft cabin. A large tarpaulin can easily be draped over the wing and staked down to form a very roomy "A"-frame shelter, thus combining the shelter and airplane cabin into one living area.

Tail wheel or nose wheel?

A tail wheel (Conventional gear) airplane is generally far better under extremely rough and soft conditions than a nose wheel (Tricycle gear) airplane. However, if you are proficient and skilled in the techniques procedures mentioned in this book, know your aircraft well, have loaded the aircraft for the correct optimum centre of gravity (CG) and have the appropriate landing gear and high floatation tyres, you should be able to go pretty much anywhere in a nose wheeler where a tail dragger can, but only to a point and no further! Tail draggers can just as easily nose over or ground loop if things go pear shaped on soft or rough terrain or if incorrect braking technique is used.

The majority of retractable gear airplanes are not suitable for serious bush work as the landing gear is too weak and, due to the limited size of the wheel wells, it is not possible to fit larger tires.

Tires

A tricycle gear light aircraft should always be fitted with a nose fork that can accommodate a tire size of at least 6:00 x 6. The main tires should never be smaller than 8:00 x 6. The 8:00 x 6 and 8:50 x 6 tires are the most popular main gear tires used on most light airplanes operating into dirt and grass strips. However, they are too small for serious "off airport" bush flying. For off airport operations the mains should be minimum 29" and nose 8:50 x 6.

STC's and field approvals can be obtained for many different sizes of tundra tires as well as larger 10" rims to allow 8:50x10, 29"x10, 31"x10 or 35"x 10 tires to be fitted to many certified light aircraft.

A special heavy duty oversize nose fork, capable of accommodating up to an 8:50x6 tire, is available and STC'd for a wide range of tricycle gear aircraft. Tail draggers may need to be re-fitted with stronger tail wheel springs and a larger tail wheel and tire.

Most standard Cessna airplanes (even some C206s) come equipped with 6:00 x 6 mains and a silly little 5" nose wheel. This is fine for asphalt and hard smooth gravel strips, but could get you into serious trouble very quickly, especially on soft sand if your CoG is too far forward! If ever you find yourself having to land on soft sand with such a small nose wheel and even if you shifted all the baggage to the rear of the plane, you still run a high risk of ending up hanging upside-down from your seat belts. *(See photo on page 52)*

3. Taking off from a vehicle track with the Cessna 172, equipped with 8:50x10 main wheels and a 8:00x6" nose wheel.

4. My C170 on a rough and rocky river bar. Nothing smaller than 31" tundra tires should ever be used in this environment.

High floatation tires should never be over inflated, in fact, they should always appear as if they are under inflated. Most pilots and mechanics do not know how to service these special tires and often inflate them to the same pressure that the POH states for a normal tarmac runway tire.

These tires are specially designed to absorb objects, such as small rocks and similar sized debris on the surface including rough and soft sand and tufts of wild grass etc. If they are over inflated they cannot do what they were designed for and in addition will wear out rapidly on hard surfaces.

Another advantage of fitting bigger tires is the higher propeller clearance and this also allows the fitting of a longer propeller.

However, there are some negatives that come along with tires over 26" in size, including loss of braking action and possibly longer take-off runs due to friction and drag. If it is really necessary to fit bigger tires, the 26" x 6 or 8:50 x 10 are good all terrain tires. In most cases I have found that 8:50 x 6 tyres are a very good general purpose tire for most regular light aircraft operating on backcountry strips.

For the more extreme, rough and wild terrain at least 31" tundra tires and bigger are required and this is definitely where the taildragger takes over.

Brakes

The larger the tire diameter, the more braking power is required. Depending on the type of brake system fitted to your airplane and the choice of oversize high floatation tires you intend to use, you may need to upgrade to a heavy duty brake system consisting of thicker discs, dual or double puck slave cylinders and brake pads.

During the pre-flight inspection frequently carefully check the brake pedal play and travel, brake pad and rotor disc wear as well as the level of fluid in the reservoirs and brake lines for scuffing and leaks.

Always apply brakes on short final approach to check that there is pressure. You do not want to discover you don't have any brakes after landing on a short one-way-in-one-way-out strip. For very short landings apply and hold a little brake pressure prior to landing and maintain it until touchdown. Be very careful using this technique in a tail dragger as you could easily nose over!

Flaps

Flaps (combined with ground effect) is one of the most important tools in STOL operations. Mechanical flaps that use the Johnson bar lever system are the best for bush flying as you can apply or retract the flaps instantly at any given time without delay, thus getting the airplane into the air or onto the ground shorter and quicker than in an airplane equipped with electric or hydraulic flaps. Other advantages is that it's fail safe as you will not lose your flaps due to electrical failure, also the mechanical system weighs less.

Cessnas have exceptionally effective Fowler flaps. The older models allow for flap deflection up to 40 degrees. In an attempt to reduce the risk of inexperienced pilots getting behind the power/drag curve especially during a go-around, Cessna reduced the maximum flap deflection from 40 degrees to 30 degrees on later models. The older model Cessnas with 40 degree flaps have a much better STOL capability than the newer models of today. The USAF Cessna L-19

"Bird dog" had modified C172/C170 wings with a 60 degree hinged fowler flap.

Retracting the flaps at the touch down spot normally gets the aircraft onto the ground immediately due to an instant loss of lift and raising the stall speed and allowing maximum weight on the wheels for braking. When retracting the flaps prior to touchdown make sure that you are not too high above the ground, otherwise this technique may result in a hard landing!

To determine the optimum flap setting for maximum lift with minimum drag on a general aviation light aircraft, fully deflect the ailerons to one side and then lower the flaps to equal the aileron deflection. (This is normally about 10-12° in a general aviation light aircraft).

STOL modifications

Many pilots believe that one can simply buy short field capabilities by installing a "STOL kit" (Short Take-Off & Landing modification) on their airplane such as a Leading Edge Cuff and Vortex Generators. Actually, the only way to master extreme short field take-offs and landings is to acquire the required skills by experience.

Before you go out and spend big bucks on all sorts of STOL mods for your airplane first learn to fly it proficiently and safely in standard form.

A skilled and experienced bush pilot in an airplane without any STOL modifications may be able to take-off and land shorter and generally out-fly any inexperienced pilot with an aircraft equipped with STOL modifications. However, on the other hand STOL modifications can be of even greater advantage to the already skilled and experienced bush pilot.

Propellers

The stock fixed pitch propeller that is fitted to most light aircraft 4-stroke reciprocating piston engines may not always be suitable for bush work or high altitude applications, as they are most often too short or have a coarse pitch (cruise prop) which is only suitable for normal length runways at low elevations and cruising. If you intend to go into any short strips especially at high elevations then at least have a local propeller shop re-pitch your metal propeller to a finer pitch (climb propeller), so that you will obtain a higher static RPM and have a better take-off and climb. Of course the downside is that you may lose a bit on your cruise speed and use more fuel but gain on ground roll and climb.

McCauley can supply a long 80" metal propeller with up to a 40° pitch. It is used mainly on light float planes. This propeller is also known as the "Borer prop" named after Rodger Borer who designed and obtained the STC for it back in 1967 in the USA.

Piston Engine Propellers typically operate at between 2500 & 2700 RPM. A piston engine with a typical red line speed of 2700 rpm should produce about 2350 rpm on the brakes. This is an indication that the engine is fitted with a "Climb prop". If the RPM indicates about 2250 or goes only just into the green arc, it is most likely a "cruise prop".

The finer the pitch angle, the higher the RPM, resulting in more power the engine will produce during the take-off and climb. However, if the pitch is adjusted too fine then although you will have an amazing take-off and climb, the engine may exceed red line in the cruise, your cruising speed will be reduced and your fuel consumption will increase, like driving your car in a lower gear the whole time. There is a trade off between climb power and cruise power therefore you need to find the optimum propeller length and pitch.

If your aircraft is fitted with a variable pitch constant speed propeller, check that your engine RPM indicates red line prior to take-off. If not, first have the RPM gauge checked for accuracy. If the RPM does not reach red line, the engine may not be delivering full power and you may need to adjust the constant speed unit (CSU). *Refer to Low power, low manifold pressure & low RPM on page 200.*

Turbine engine propellers are larger in length and width and typically operate between 1500 and 2000 RPM whilst the engines gas generator shaft turns at about 37000 RPM and is indicated on the "N1" or Ng" gauge. The "N1" or gas generator speed is read as a percent of r.p.m. In the Pratt & Whitney PT-6 engine, it is based on a figure of 37,000 r.p.m. at 100 percent. On a turboprop engine the propeller RPM is not an indication of engine power. Turboprop engine power is indicated by a torque-meter.

Engine power modifications

A question often asked by pilots operating out of short high elevation strips is "How can I reliably get more power from my engine?"

If you intend to build a true high performance "hot rod" engine that is capable of producing the most horse power possible, the engine will need to be totally stripped down and rebuilt from scratch. Every moving part of the engine will need to be carefully machined and balanced. The camshaft lobe lift and profile should be modified, new cylinders with high compression pistons installed and the intake ports and induction flow balanced. The propeller length and pitch is a major consideration, especially a fixed pitch propeller. At least one magneto should be replaced with an electronic ignition unit. Cylinders and oil cooling are also major considerations.

At the end of the day a 50% increase in horse power is very easily and reliably obtainable from a typical normally aspirated aircraft piston engine. Below a few basic "bolt on" ideas.

Propeller

The easiest and cheapest way to get an instant horse power boost from an engine fitted with a metal fixed pitch propeller is by re-pitching the propeller blades to a finer pitch to allow the engine to turn faster (more rpm). The engine will now produce more HP and the propeller will produce more thrust. This will give your airplane a much better and safer short field take-off and climb. However, you may have a slower cruise speed so in order to go as fast as before you would need to run the engine at or above red line so it will use more fuel. An engine fitted with a constant speed or basic variable pitch prop should obtain red line RPM on the take-off.

High compression pistons

The easiest way to get an instant big horse power boost is by simply changing the stock low compression pistons with high compression pistons. Most standard aircraft engines have a typical compression ratio (CR) of 7:1. There are supplemental type certificated (STC) pistons on the market available for a handful of engines, but are generally not higher than 8.5:1. If you are running your engine on Mogas, you may not be able to do so any longer. Any compression ratio higher than about 8.5:1 in a traditional aircraft engine would require the higher octane in Avgas to reduce the risk of detonation. A water-methanol injection system may prevent detonation from occurring when running high compressions and advanced timing on regular Mogas.

There are high quality - high performance forged pistons with compression ratios of up to 10:1 or more available for just about any aircraft engine. These pistons are used in many experimental "hot rod" engines fitted to STOL aircraft and racing aircraft. Fitting high compression pistons with a CR of around 10:1 to a standard 150hp aircraft engine that originally had 7:1 CR pistons may produce an instant 180hp!

Free-flow tuned exhaust system

Fitting a properly tuned free flow exhaust system can increase the engine horse power considerably. There is a fair amount of science involved and if it is not designed and built 100% correctly the benefits may be marginal. There are systems on the market approved for many certified aircraft engines, but they are very expensive. On a six cylinder engine you could take all the pipes from each cylinder, terminate them all together or three per side into a tail pipe and obtain a conservative increase in HP. This is a neutral free-flow system. An additional advantage to a tuned or neutral system is that the engine exhaust noise may be quieter.

Part 2. Aircraft operation

Familiarization & test flight - exploring the flight envelope

It is of paramount importance that before you attempt to do any low and slow manoeuvring, flying in challenging confined areas or strips, you first get to know your aircraft exceptionally well, especially indicated airspeeds and how the aircraft responds and reacts when approaching or during various stall configurations. You need to fully explore the lower end of the performance envelope of the aircraft. I cannot emphasize enough how important this exercise is. This is the very first exercise that we do during all my Advanced Flying Courses.

You should never attempt to land on marginal strips especially one-way-in-one-way-out strips using or relying on normal indicated approach speeds. You may frequently have to use indicated airspeeds that are much lower to what you are used to, therefore you need to be comfortable with what you see on your ASI. A pilot who intends to perform any short field operations needs to posses the advanced skill required to be able to fly and control the aircraft safely at very slow airspeeds and who furthermore should be able to do so without solely referring to the ASI!

First load sufficient ballast in the rear of the aircraft (refer also to Stall speeds and Ballast on page 40 & 42), then practice various configurations of stalls between zero and and full flaps, power off and power on. Carefully observe and record the indicated airspeeds during the approach to stall (stall warning) and when the airplane actually stalls. You will be amazed of the indicated speeds that the airplane stalls at. Sometimes the ASI can indicate zero, especially when flying with full flaps and full power ("hanging on the prop"). This is caused by what is known as "position error" of the pitot tube. Position error occurs when the wing is at a slow flight high angle of attack and the air impacting the pitot tube does so at an angle causing the airspeed indicator to read low.

Although the indicated airspeed may be a lot lower than the true airspeed or ground speed, the true stall speed will still be less with power on. There is a remarkable difference in the power-on and power-off stall speeds in propeller driven aircraft. Power reduces the stall speed because the propeller slipstream speeds up the air flowing over the wings which delays the stall. Inexperienced pilots should exercise caution when practicing full power-on stalls as some aircraft wings stall from the tip resulting in a very dramatic and rapid wing drop and could end up in an inverted spin if not corrected immediately.

Practice incipient, half and full revolution spins and recovery with minimum loss of altitude. Practice full flap, full power stalls and recovery with minimum loss of altitude. Practice extremely slow flying just above the stall using power to maintain altitude and pitch to maintain speed, including turns left and right. Practice flying just above the stall in ground effect over a long runway. Always take notice of and record of the indicated airspeeds on your ASI.

You must become one with your aircraft like "hand in glove" prior to attempting any serious short take-offs or landings in one-way-in-one-way-out strips or "off airport" operations. Your aircraft should be an extension of you, not you an extension of your aircraft. Never allow the aircraft to get ahead of you! Always be ahead of the aircraft and situation. Use the numbers you see on your ASI only as a reference, as it is not a true speed. Learn to feel what the airplane is doing or is about to do. Learn to fly by feel ("Seat of pants flying"). Practice take-offs, approaches and landings without your ASI.

The test flight

Prior to the test flight make a copy the following table, so that you can document and record all the indicated airspeeds and other data. Flap positions differ on various aircraft.

Flaps Position and Power Setting. Wings level.	Stall Warning Indicated Airspeed	Actual Stall Indicated Airspeed
0 Flap Power off		
10° / 1st notch Flap Power off		
50% Flap Power off		
Full Flap Power off		
Full Flap and Full power		
Optimum Take-Off Speed		
Minimum Controllable Slow Flight Speed – Full flap and power as required		
Power Setting during Slow Flight		
Indicated Airspeed during a 55-60 degree steep turn with half flap and power as required to maintain altitude and remain off the stall		
Best Glide Speed, 0 Flap		
Minimum Safe Stabilized Approach Speed		
Power setting at Minimum Safe Stabilized Approach Speed		
VSI / Rate of descent at Minimum Safe Stabilized Approach Speed		
Optimum Stabilized Approach Speed		
Power Setting at Optimum Stabilized Approach Speed		
VSI / Rate of descent at Optimum Stabilized Approach Speed		
Indicated stall speed in ground effect with power off and stick fully back		
Indicated stall speed in ground effect with power on, holding-off		

Stall Speeds

Do you know what the slowest indicated stall speed is for your aircraft, wings level full flap?

Unknown to most pilots there are in fact four stall speeds as follows:

1. The first and highest stall speed is the "Vso" stall speed as printed in the Pilots Operating Handbook (POH) which is usually based on wings level, full flaps, power off, "utility category" with no weight in the rear of the aircraft.
2. The next lower stall speed is with optimum rear CG, weight or ballast in the rear of the aircraft.
3. The next lower stall speed is with optimum rear CG, weight or ballast in the rear of the aircraft and power on ("hanging on the prop").
4. Finally the lowest stall speed is with optimum rear CG, weight or ballast in the rear of the aircraft, power on ("hanging on the prop") in Ground Effect!

Stall speeds are affected by:

- aircraft weight
- positioning of weight inside the aircraft (CG)
- flaps
- power

Centre of Gravity

Stall speeds are affected by the centre of gravity. Never load the aircraft outside of its Centre of Gravity (CG) as this is extremely dangerous, especially at slower speeds! An aircraft with a properly balanced CG will take-off, fly and land better than an aircraft with a too forward or rear CG.

Effects of CG too far forward:

- Nose heavy resulting in flat landings when the power is cut and excessive up elevator control.
- Increased drag created by excessive elevator control.
- Application of power is required to prevent nose from dropping.
- Higher Stall speed.
- Increased fuel consumption and decrease in range.

Effects of CG too far aft:

- Dangerous and unrecoverable stall and possibly resulting in a flat spin.
- High risk of running out of forward elevator control at slower speeds, especially during take-off or landing.
- Increased drag created by excessive elevator control.
- Increased fuel consumption and decrease in range.
- Increased landing distance.
- A higher landing speed is required to keep the tail up.
- Possibility of the tail hitting the ground during the landing.
- Possibility of the tail settling onto the ground after shutting the engine down.

Optimum aft CG is better than a forward CG as it leads to:

- lower stall speeds,
- lighter elevator control,
- less drag,
- better lift generated by wings.

Ballast

Determining how much ballast you need in the rear of your aircraft.

An aircraft with only one or two people occupying the two front pilot seats and no weight in the rear will definitely be nose heavy under slow flight conditions.

I have found that in most 4-seater aircraft you need approximately 20kg / 44lbs of ballast and 40kg / 88lbs in a 6-seater. The ballast should be as far aft as possible in the baggage compartment. Keep in mind that the CG may change as fuel is consumed so this should also be considered during this exercise.

First start with an empty aircraft with only two persons up front and no weight in the rear. Apply full flap and trim the elevator so that it will glide at and maintain the slowest speed possible "hands off" without the nose wanting to drop and causing an increase in airspeed. Note the indicated airspeed. Now load about 20kg / 44lbs in the baggage compartment and do the same exercise again, adding a little more weight noting the indicated airspeed. You should now notice a slower indicated airspeed. Continue increasing the ballast until the aircraft can maintain an almost hands-off glide approach just above stall.

You will now have determined the optimum ballast to use in your aircraft when flying with no weight in the rear and also the optimum CG for your aircraft. Using the CG chart in your aircraft POH calculate the weight and balance and ensure that the CG is within the safe limits. For future reference, no matter how much weight you have in the aircraft, you should always attempt to try maintain this optimum aft CG position for safe STOL operations.

Stabilized approach

This is not to be confused with a "smooth" or "stable" approach during calm air conditions. Many pilots have a very bad habit of, after setting up an almost perfect initial approach, inducing "turbulence" upon reaching short final approach by over controlling roll, pitch and power, resulting in a totally uncoordinated rolling, pitching and yawing approach to land, even in stable atmospheric conditions. I call this habit "Pilot Induced Turbulence" (PIT).

A stabilized approach is a steeper than normal nose down approach in which the aircraft is in a position where minimum input of all controls will result in a safe and almost perfect landing. Normally the best approach angle is around 4 - 4.5 degrees. Basically, once power and pitch is set you should be able to take your hands off all controls and the plane should continue on a smooth nose low descent towards the touchdown spot all by itself without a tendency of the airspeed increasing! Only very fine and smooth adjustments may be necessary. You will need to develop the feel for exactly when and how much throttle to use, especially on turbine engined aircraft.

Provided the aircraft is properly loaded or there is sufficient ballast in the rear, all you would need to do is round out into a flare using your little finger on the control wheel or stick and experience perfect smooth touchdown without even adjusting the power setting! It is not possible to maintain a stabilized approach at the Optimum Stabilized Approach Speed without sufficient weight or ballast in the rear of the aircraft. In a nose heavy aircraft the nose will drop when you cut the power and the aircraft may land flat and may result in a bounced landing.

Some advantages of a stabilized approach are:
- the aircraft is always in a nose low position, so no chance of getting behind the drag curve,
- continuous and better visibility of the touch down area,
- less workload,
- good landings every time,
- in the event of an engine failure and after retracting drag flap you should still be able to glide to the touch down spot.

I often demonstrate a completely "hands off" landing by setting up a stabilized approach and allowing the aircraft to actually approach and land by itself without touching or adjusting any flight or engine control. It may not be the smoothest landing, but it will be a safe landing. Therefore a stabilized approach is an approach in which the aircraft is in a position where minimum input of all controls will result in a safe landing.

There is no better or safer approach than a "Stabilized Approach"!

How to set up a "Stabilized Approach", determine the "Optimum Stabilized Approach Speed" and the "Minimum Safe Stabilized Approach Speed"

Windshield mark

Note: This windshield mark should only be used in the beginning of the exercise to assist you in getting familiar with this technique, then the mark should be removed. An experienced pilot should be able to set up a stabilized approach in any aircraft without ever using this method.

The windshield mark is a mark made on the windshield and used to aim and align the airplane with the aiming point or touch down spot. To determine the correct position for this mark, set up a cruise flight with constant altitude, cruise power and airspeed, then determine where the horizon intersects the windshield. Using a whiteboard marker or grease pencil, make a 50mm / 2" horizontal line about 10mm / ½" below the horizon on the windshield in front of your field of view, then make a '+' in the middle of the line.

During a stabilized approach the windshield mark should remain aligned with the spot on the ground throughout the descent regardless of flap selection. This technique is also referred to as "rifle sighting" the touchdown spot.

Ensure that the aircraft is correctly loaded (optimum aft CG).

A stabilized approach must be set up with a slightly higher than normal glide slope. The nose of the aircraft must at ALL times be pointing down during the approach so that the pilot can continuously see the touchdown spot until almost in ground effect.

Setting up the Stabilized Approach for the first time

1. Start with a higher than normal and very long final approach with full flaps and the nose pointing down at the aiming point.

2. Cut the power and slowly raise the nose to slow down the approach speed without ballooning out of the glide path. As soon as the aircraft starts to sink or drop out of the glide path note the indicated airspeed and round it off to the next highest number. This is the Minimum Indicated Safe Stabilized Approach Speed. At this time the nose will be flat and you will now be just on top of the drag curve. Immediately apply power and lower the nose so that it once again points down at the aiming point and re-establish the Stabilized Approach.

3. Now set the power and trim so that the "Windshield Mark" is lined up with the aiming point with a continuous vertical descent rate of approximately 500-700ft per minute, then note the indicated airspeed. This is now your "Optimum Indicated Approach Speed" to maintain a Stabilized Approach.

4. Document and remember the power setting (RPM / Percent power), rate of descent (VSI) and indicated airspeed (ASI). The rate of descent and indicated airspeed should always remain the same whilst the power setting may change depending on the air temperature and wind direction etc.

Side slipping

Side slipping is an effective way of losing altitude and speed very quickly. Most pilots are a bit apprehensive to use this maneuver to the full effect mainly because they were never really shown how to do it properly.

It is important to remember that if you are too high and too fast, you would need to raise the nose slightly during the side slip in order to decrease your speed during the descent. Otherwise, when you come out of the side slip, you may be at the right height, but still too fast. (By lowering the nose you will increase your speed.)

Another interesting point is that most aircraft cannot maintain the extended runway centreline during a full side slip, so it is better to first apply full rudder allowing the airplane to fly off the centreline and then apply a lot of aileron. If done correctly, the aeroplane should converge back onto the centreline during the side slip.

Ground Effect

Ground effect is one of the most important tools in extreme short field take-off and landing (STOL) operations! Ground effect occurs from the ground up to within half the wing span of the airplane.

Ground effect is caused by the ground interference of the airflow around the aircraft. Contrary to common belief, ground effect is not a "cushion of air" between the bottom of the wings and the ground. It is created from wing downwash and wingtip vortices.

As long as the aircraft is in ground effect it can actually fly below the true power on (out of ground effect) stall speed! This allows for much shorter than normal take-offs and landings.

A short field ground effect take-off is achieved by allowing or rather forcing the aircraft to become airborne well under the normal lift-off speed whilst remaining only a few feet off the ground until the airplane has accelerated to a safe out-of-ground-effect climb speed.

A short field ground effect landing (also known as a "Short Spot Landing") is achieved when (conditions permitting) the airplane is able to descend into ground effect a few feet of the ground about

75m / 250ft prior to the threshold or touch down spot, then slowing the airplane down to under the (out of ground effect) stall speed by carefully raising the angle of attack and smoothly applying power to keep the airplane flying about 3ft/1m above the surface. As you arrive over the touch down spot, you simply cut the power and the aircraft should immediately stall onto the ground in a nose high attitude without any floating or hold-off.

Note that the aircraft will only be able to land in a nose high attitude with power off if you have sufficient weight or ballast at the rear of the plane (Optimum aft CG). In other words, provided it is not "nose heavy" (CG too far forward).

Ground effect take-offs and landings are described in more detail later on in this book.

Runway length

A safe rule of thumb when operating from a short strip is that if you obtain 70% of rotation speed at the halfway point of the runway, you can take-off in the remaining distance. If you have not reached 70% of your take-off speed by the halfway mark, you should be able to abort and stop before the end of the strip. Remember to cut all the power, retract all flaps and apply hard braking without locking up the wheels.

Take-off distance

Rules of thumb:

- Down-slope take-off distance is reduced by about 5% per degree of slope.
- Up-slope take-off distance is increased by about 7% per degree of slope.
- Cut grass – add 7%

- Rough, rocky, or grass tufts – add 10%
- Long grass - add 25%
- Sand – add 15%
- Soft sand – add 45%
- Mud or snow – add 50% or more

Unimproved soft and rough surfaces (off airport landing sites)

Also known as "off airport operations", means anywhere other than a prepared landing site, strip or runway such as beaches, dry river beds, gravel bars, salt pans, fields, dirt tracks, roads etc.

Your aircraft should be fully equipped for the type of terrain and surface that you intend to land on. For example, if you intend to land on soft sand or very rough surfaces, ensure that you have the appropriate tyres for the job. The tyre pressure must be low, so that the tyre tread pattern is as wide and oval as possible on soft sand and can easily absorb rough ground or objects such as small rocks.

On a nose wheel airplane, always pack as much weight in the rear of the plane as possible, within the C of G, this will assist in keeping weight off the nose wheel.

You want to keep the nose as light as possible at ALL times during take-off, landing and taxiing on a soft or rough surface.

When attempting to land on an unimproved area for the first time, first do a few inspection runs to check the surface for soft sand, holes, termite mounds, rocks, bushes, debris etc.

When landing on a beach it is advisable to do so during low tide. The best part of the beach to land on is the grey, smooth and hard sand

5. The C172 equipped with 8:50x6" main tyres and 600x6" nose wheel on a dry gravel / sand river bed.

6. The C170 with 31" Tundra tyres on very soft sand in a dry river bed.

between the white wavy soft sand and the wet shiny sand towards the water. Do a touch and go with about half flaps, keeping the nose high after touchdown with a bit of power on. Observe the ground ahead of you and under the main wheels, then execute a go-around and come back and fly low over your tracks and observe the depth.

Once you are satisfied that the surface is suitable then commit to a full stop landing with full flaps, power on and nose high attitude. Depending on the amount of slope the beach has you may have to apply quite a lot of rudder towards the higher ground to prevent the airplane from wanting to veer off towards the water. (See *photo 3.)*

Keep the stick fully back after landing and the flaps partially to fully extended with moderate braking. Stop straight ahead in the direction of the landing. Do not taxi the aircraft unless you are 100% sure there are no obstacles in front of you or that you are not going to get stuck. Rather shut down the aircraft, get out and inspect the surface.

If necessary, use your axe, saw, bush knife and shovel to clean and prepare the best suitable area and surface to use for taxi, parking, take-off and future landings.

Prior to taking off again in a nose wheeler from a very soft or muddy surface, it may be a good idea to first tie up the nose wheel fork with rope to prevent the oleo from extending as the nose is raised during the take-off roll. This trick will enable you to get the nose wheel off the ground very early whilst still maintaining a lower angle of attack, preventing over rotation and excessive drag. (See *photo 8.)*

7. Keep the nose as light as possible by loading sufficient weight or ballast in the rear of the airplane to avoid the nose wheel digging in. Especially if the airplane has a small nose wheel!

8. Example of a nose wheel fork tied up to prevent the oleo from extending during the take-off roll from a very soft or muddy surface.

Taxiing

Whether a tail dragger or nose wheeler, regardless to surface condition, but especially on rough and soft areas always taxi with the stick fully back at all times, except when a strong wind calls for a different procedure. *Refer to your POH for the standard procedure.*

Securing an airplane

Most pilots believe, and were taught, that you must always point the nose of the plane into the wind. I totally disagree with this. When mooring an airplane, don't point the nose into the wind unless you want the plane to become airborne in a strong wind. Remember that the airplane will not fly in reverse so if the tail end is facing the wind the airplane will not fly! Ensure that the tail is very securely tied down and gust-locked.

Another ridiculous way of tying down an airplane is to use concrete blocks. Unless these blocks weigh many times more than the aircraft itself I don't see them being of much help in preventing the airplane from becoming airborne. You might as well just load the blocks into the plane and not bother tying it down as it will have the same effect!

If you have to face the airplane into a possible storm or gale force wind, cut down two long thin trees or find two pipes or poles and strap them to the tops of the wings directly on top of the spar section running from the wing root to the tips. Cheap light weight swimming pool noodles with a plastic conduit through the centre can easily be stowed in the rear of the plane. This will act as a highly effective "air brake" or "spoiler" and will prevent the wings from flying! In addition chock with rocks/blocks etc. on both sides of all wheels. (See *photo 9.)*

Always carry at least three lengths of 12mm / 1/2" marine or mountain climbing rope. Ski rope is not strong enough, this is only useful for securing the tail section to a tree or securing branches or a pole to the top of the wings.

A standard hitch knot consisting of a round turn and two half hitch turns is normally sufficient for most tie down applications. Under more severe conditions a "Hurricane hitch" knot may be desired.

Examples of securing airplanes prior to an approaching storm.

9. Swimming pool noodles are light weight and can be easily stowed in the rear of the plane ready to use at any time.

10.

Note the "hurricane hitch knots" around the wing strut using marine rope and the logs on top of the wings to act as spoilers to break the airflow over the wings. However, the ground anchor is of more importance. Tree stumps or large boulders are the strongest anchors.

*11. Ratchet tie down straps may look very pro, however, it's one of the worst.
During a severe storm, the rocking motion of the wings will cause the hooks
to fall out of the anchor. Straps may also be weaker and heavier than good quality
marine rope.*

Long spring steel military tent pegs make good anchors if there is nothing better available. Try to tie the tail down with a peg as well as to a tree or fence pole. The tie down ropes should be secured to the pegs about 45° away from the tie down ring towards the wing tip. Tie down blocks that take 3 steel anchor pegs each at a 45° angle are the strongest type available, these should be placed directly under the wing tie down ring. Under severe wind conditions it is advisable to tie the rope through and around the wing strut! This may prevent the rope from snapping off at the ring. (See *photo 9b.*)

It's also a good idea to tie down the nose of a tricycle gear airplane and some airplanes actually have tie down rings under the nose section just behind the nose wheel. This will prevent the nose from rising and thus increasing the angle of attack which may cause the airplane to become airborne early.

Under severe weather conditions out in the bush it may be better (if possible) to locate 2 trees about 10m / 25ft apart in an area where you can park the airplane then cut the trees down to about 2ft. Use the stumps as tie down anchors and cut wedge shaped slits into the sides to prevent the rope from pulling off. It would be a bonus if you have one at the rear of the plane, too. This the strongest natural tie down anchors you'll ever find anywhere.

If you are planning to abandon the airplane somewhere where there are wild animals, it may be a good idea to place thorny branches around the tires. Some animals like to chew on tires.

Hand starting the engine

Even if you have a second pilot or a responsible person, never trust the brakes, always use chocks or rocks and even tie downs. You can never be safe enough.

Prime the engine as per the POH, throttle closed, magnetos in OFF position and mixture cut off carefully, turn the propeller through 2-4 compressions (suitable for 4 or 6 cylinder engines) until the propeller is in approximately a 45° position and just before the next compression stroke. Remember, whilst priming the cylinders or any other time you need to turn the propeller, you should treat the propeller as live at all times!

Standing in front and slightly left of the propeller and with the propeller at a comfortable high position before compression: magnetos on, mixture full, throttle set as per the POH (approximately 1/4"/ 6-8mm).

Wear leather gloves. If you don't have gloves, use the oil rag or something similar. The trailing edge of a propeller can cut your fingers.

Raise your left leg slightly and place your hands about half to two thirds way up the propeller, using as much momentum as possible, yank the propeller down by swinging your left leg backwards at the same time. After the engine starts, you should find yourself a safe distance away from the propeller.

If engine fails to start then do not prime again. Instead just turn the magnetos off and pull the mixture to cut-off, then carefully turn the propeller to the next suitable start position and try again.

Take-offs and landings

DISCLAIMER AND WARNING!

The techniques described in the following section are of an extreme and highly advanced nature. The use of these techniques may be hazardous to non proficient and inexperienced pilots.

Refer to the *Disclaimer and Warning* in the beginning of this book before attempting any maneuvers or techniques described in this book.

Part 3. Take-offs and landings

The following techniques apply to most general aviation light to medium size aircraft. Under reasonable conditions (i.e. between sea level and up to about 2500ft asl and temperatures under 30°C / 88°F) many popular *certified* general aviation 4-8 place single and twin engine light aircraft are able to take-off and land within 250m / 660ft.

For example a lightly loaded standard Super Cub, Huskey, Maule, Cessna 170, 180, 182, 185 and 206 without any STOL modifications can take-off in 200m / 600ft and land within 100m / 300ft on a dry hard or grass surface with no wind at an average elevation of between sea level and up to about 2500ft asl. A Cessna 210, Piper Cherokee-Six, twin engined Piper Seneca and Norman Islander can take-off in under 250m / 660ft and land in 100-150m/300-500ft . The Cessna Caravan, LET 410 or Twin Otter can take-off in under 300m / 900ft and land to a full stop in under 150m / 450ft.

These are only a few examples of popular general aviation certified types.

Maximum power for take-off (4-stroke reciprocating engine)

Here are some tips to achieve maximum available power for an extreme short field take-off.

Firstly warm the engine up to normal operating oil temperature and not just Cylinder Head Temperature (CHT). A hot engine produces more hp than a cold engine. Hot oil is thinner than cold oil and therefore it is easier and less of an effort for the engine to drive the oil pump.

Adjusting the mixture at maximum static RPM will also give more power. A reciprocating engine's power is measured by a RPM and manifold pressure meter. Always know what the maximum static RPM should be for your airplane. The higher the static RPM, the more power you will have for the ground run and climb out. An airplane fitted with a cruise propeller is not at all suitable for short field and high elevation operations. Aircraft fitted with Variable Pitch or Constant Speed propellers should be at or very close to red line static RPM and should indicate red line RPM during the climb out. A turbo charged engine is able to produce more power by boosting the manifold pressure. Do not over lean a turbo charged engine on take-off. Refer to the POH for information on leaning the mixture for take-off.

Turning off all lights and unnecessary electrical equipment will allow the engine to produce more power for the take-off because the engine will not be labouring to drive the generator or alternator to supply current to compensate for the discharge from the battery. In fact, during an extreme short field situation and especially when the Amp meter is indicating a positive charge rate it may be necessary to disable the alternator or generator by turning it off or turning off the master switch. If taking off at night, the lights can still be operated whilst the alternator or generator is disabled. Once safely established on the climb out, the landing lights can be turned off and the alternator turned back on to charge the battery.

If the airplane is equipped with an air conditioner, never take-off under any conditions with it turned on. Air conditioners drain a large amount of horse power from the engine. A bush plane should not have an air conditioner anyway, as it's just 'dead weight'.

The cooler (more dense) the outside air temperature, the more power the engine will deliver and the more efficient the propeller will be.

Maximum power for take-off (turbine / turboprop engine)

Turboprop engine power output is measured by a Torque-meter. Torque-meters are calibrated in percentage units, foot-pounds or psi. Turbine engines maximum take-off power is limited mostly by the temperature of the turbine section or Interstage Turbine Temperature (ITT). This is monitored via an ITT gauge.

The temperature of the turbine section must be monitored very closely to prevent overheating the turbine blades and other exhaust section components during the start and take-off.

Optimum speed for short field take-offs

This is the speed that the aircraft will become airborne in ground effect, but which is not sufficient to climb out of ground effect. This speed is below the out of ground effect power on stall speed for a particular flap setting of the airplane.

When performing a very short field take-off you should not refer to the ASI for rotation speed. Instead you should maintain a positive back pressure on the control stick or wheel for a nose wheeler and a neutral position for a tail dragger. When the airplane is ready to fly, apply flaps as required to help lift it off the ground early. Keep the airplane in ground effect and slowly retract flaps so that the airplane can quickly accelerate to a safe climb speed.

Optimum speed for short field landings

The optimum speed prior to touch down during a short field landing is just on the tip of the stall with a fair amount of power on. Any more speed than this may result in the airplane floating past the touchdown spot as well as requiring more space to roll to a stop during braking.

If you end up floating and have to cut the power and "hold off" until the speed decays towards a stall then you simply not performing a short field landing anymore. If this happens then you should retract the flaps immediately to force the airplane to land.

During a proper short field landing you "hold off" with power not pitch as you are behind the drag curve in the "region of reverse command". The objective is to aim for a spot and touchdown on that spot. Therefore only maintain absolute minimum speed to keep the aircraft flying.

Rules of thumb:

A 10% increase in touchdown speed equals a 20% increase in landing distance.

Add 2% to the indicated airspeed for each 1,000 feet of density altitude to determine the true airspeed. Always use the same indicated airspeed for all landings regardless of the altitude.

Optimum height above the ground at the touchdown spot

Always plan to arrive over the touchdown spot as low and slow as possible above the ground. The main wheels of the aircraft should be no higher than about 1m / 3ft above the ground when you cut the power. It is common during a short field landing to have the tail wheel already on the ground prior to touch down. This is due to the high angle of attack obtained when approaching a power on stall.

Warning: Anything higher than this may result in a hard landing or bounce and possibly a crash!

12 & 13. The optimum height above the ground to cut the power during a slow short field landing. Note in these photos, 40 flap, elevator is fully aft , "hanging on the prop" with power on.

Twin-engine Short Take-Off and Landing (STOL) operations

Any pilot planning to perform any STOL operations in a twin-engine aircraft should become exceptionally proficient and skilled with the aircraft, in particular the emergency procedures. Such a pilot should at every opportunity practice simulated engine failure and procedures. The most dangerous phase during a short field take-off and landing in a twin-engine aircraft is flying at or below Vmc "Red Line" speed.

Vmc is the minimum airspeed at which the aircraft's directional control can be maintained when the critical engine is inoperative and the other is operating at full power. At speeds below Vmc, the rudder is no longer able to overcome the asymmetrical yawing force produced by the remaining operating engine.

Although twin-engine aircraft should never take-off before reaching Vmc, it may be necessary during an extreme short field take-off. If this is necessary, the nose should be lowered immediately after take-off and the aircraft accelerated in ground effect to above the red line as quickly as possible whilst slowly retracting drag flap and further accelerating to above blue line.

Vyse "Blue Line" is the best single-engine climb speed when flying with one engine inoperative and the other operating at full power. Vyse and Vmc is determined with the aircraft at maximum gross weight, which is a worst-case scenario because the heavier the aircraft, the higher the Vyse and Vmc.

Airspeeds between Vmc and Vyse are considered a danger zone during the take-off, especially at or close to MAUW. That's because if your aircraft lost an engine during takeoff while flying between these two V speeds, you would be dangerously close to Vmc and not be able to achieve your single-engine maximum climb rate. Without some altitude, there is little or no room for recovery or climbing above obstacles on the ground. The pilot in command must have a clear emergency plan prior to take-off regarding engine failure.

Some STOL twins have such a slow Vmc (such as the BN2A Britten Norman Islander for example with only 39 knots) that they don't even have a Vmc speed when operated fairly empty. In fact, you can actually "hang on the prop" of the good engine all the way down to stall and still maintain control!

Landing some piston and turboprop twin-engine airplanes can result in a premature, hard touchdown if the engines are brought back to idle too soon. This is because large propellers spinning rapidly in low pitch create considerable drag. In such airplanes it may be preferable to maintain power throughout the landing flare and touchdown. Once on the ground, propeller beta range operation on a turbine twin will dramatically reduce the need for braking in comparison to piston airplanes of similar weights.

14. BN2A Britten Norman Islander 10 seater STOL twin.

TAKE-OFFS

Optimum performance take-off

An "Optimum Performance Take-Off" is precision take-off achieved by allowing the aircraft to take-off when it is ready to fly rather than the normal sloppy take-off using up excessive and unnecessary runway distance and pulling back on the stick/yoke at a given indicated airspeed. Too many pilots use excessively high take-off speeds resulting in forcing the aircraft to remain on the runway for far too long. The most common reason for this bad habit is bad instruction!

To perform an Optimum Performance Take-Off and determine the "Optimum Indicated Take-Off Speed" for your aircraft apply 1ˢᵗ notch of flap which is the "Optimum Take-off Flap Setting", then apply "Optimum Elevator Deflection" (applicable to nose wheel airplanes only), which should be no more than a fully deflected aileron.

Release the brakes and smoothly apply power during the start of the roll. As the speed of the airflow over the horizontal stabilizer increases it will start pushing the elevator down causing the stick / yoke to move forward, so you may need to add back pressure on the stick/yoke to maintain elevator position, otherwise the nose will not rise when it should, resulting in the airplane not taking off and continue to use up runway.

Allow the nose to rise to no more than about 5-7 degrees and then simply hold it in this attitude until the aircraft flies itself off the ground. For a tail wheel aircraft the stick is held back and then moved forward during the roll to raise the tail to the same 5-7 degree attitude.

As soon as the wheels leave the surface note and record the indicated airspeed, this is the "Optimum Indicated Take-off Speed" for your aircraft. Note: In some cases, especially aircraft equipped with a STOL modification, this indicated airspeed may actually read zero or close to it. Immediately lower the nose after take-off, so that the aircraft can accelerate to climb speed.

"Optimum Control Surface Deflection" is the maximum deflection angle that will produce the best results with minimum drag. Deflection angles greater than this will result in an adverse or negative effect. This rule also applies to the "Optimum Angle of Attack" of the wings during the take-off roll. In most cases this angle is about 12-15 degrees. Increasing this angle at any time during the take-off roll will result in excessive drag and an increase of the take-off roll.

A tail dragger's centre of gravity (CG) is aft of the main wheels, therefore they have a much higher tendency to yaw off the runway during the take-off roll than a nose wheeler, therefore more aggressive rudder movement is required.

A tail dragger's directional control on the ground is affected more by engine torque, propeller "P factor", gyroscopic precession and the corkscrew effect of the propeller during the take-off run than nose wheelers. Right rudder, smooth application of power and raising the tail at the correct time will help to reduce these effects. Raising the tail too early during the take-of run may result in loss of directional control.

Short field take-off

If taking off from a smooth hard surface, set flaps at 0° or 1st notch . If you are on a grass or rough surface, start with optimum lift flap setting (first notch or 10° or deflect the flaps to the same angle as a fully deflected aileron). Only apply more flap when the aircraft is ready to fly, otherwise the flaps will generate unnecessary drag during the roll and extend the roll rather than shorten it.

If possible, apply full power on the brakes and check that you are obtaining maximum available static RPM. Note that with some aircraft with powerful engines, especially tail draggers, it may not be possible to start the take-off roll with full power as the aircraft may yaw off the runway.

In addition propellers are more efficient when moving forward, so you may even see better results by applying full power after releasing the brakes. You would definitely have less propeller and horizontal stabilizer damage by using this method.

Nose wheel airplanes: Release brakes and maintain positive back-pressure on the stick, not fully back as you do not want to induce unnecessary drag or raise the nose too early. Always keep the stick at "Optimum Elevator Position". Do not refer to the ASI for rotation speed.

When the nose rises, the airplane is almost ready to fly, now apply more flaps and the aircraft will take-off on its own. For an extreme short field take-off in a nose wheeler you can use full flaps and the "un-stick" method by forcing the aircraft off the ground by momentarily and very quickly pulling the control stick or wheel further back and then forward again to the original position.

15. Taking off from a short and rough dirt trail in the C172.

16. Taking off from a road in a confined space. Note the police cars on either end to stop the traffic.

Warning: Be careful when using this technique as you can easily over-rotate and slam the tail onto the ground if not done correctly!

Tail wheel airplanes: Because of the high angle of attack of a tail dragger whilst on the ground it is necessary to raise the tail as soon as possible so as to reduce the aerodynamic drag as well as the friction caused by the tailwheel on the ground. Maintain a neutral to slightly forward stick position during the roll, after the tail rises apply more flaps and rotate at the optimum time.

Be careful not to rotate too soon or over rotate, or else you will induce drag that will lengthen your ground run as well as possibly bumping the tail back onto the ground. You must develop a feel for when your airplane is ready to fly. (For example: 1000...2000...3000 Pull! or 1 potato... 2 potato or whatever works for you.)

After lift-off, immediately and progressively lower the nose to remain in ground effect and accelerate to climb speed whilst slowly retracting the flaps back to first notch /10°.

Do not retract the flaps before first lowering the nose otherwise you may stall!

This is especially important if you have used full or "drag flap" to get airborne. Do not climb out of ground effect with full flap.

Short soft field take-off

Also refer to section on unimproved soft and rough surfaces (Off airport landing sites) on page 49.

Apply optimum lift flap (1ˢᵗ notch). Apply full power on the brakes and ensure that you have maximum static RPM.

Nose wheel airplanes: Maintain full back pressure on the stick. When the nose rises, release just enough back pressure on the stick to keep the nose wheel off the ground. Smoothly and progressively apply more flaps and help the aircraft off the ground by adding positive back pressure on the stick or wheel.

Tail wheel airplanes: Allow the tail to rise off the ground, but keep it low during the run so as to get weight off the main wheels as soon as possible. Smoothly progressively apply more flap and back pressure on the stick or wheel. Immediately lower the nose in ground effect to increase speed and slowly retract flaps to first notch/10° and climb out.

17. Taking off from a soft dry river bed.

Short field take-off over an obstacle *(see photo 16)*

Set flaps at 0° or 1ˢᵗ notch. Apply full power on the brakes and ensure that you are getting maximum RPM.

Nose wheel airplanes - Release brakes and maintain positive back pressure on the stick, but not full back pressure. As the nose rises, apply flaps and rotate or un-stick.

Tail wheel airplanes - Release brakes and maintain a slight forward stick position during the roll, when the tail rises apply flaps and rotate.

Immediately lower the nose into ground effect and retract as much flap as soon as possible in order to lose drag and accelerate quicker. Remain in ground effect increasing your speed as much as possible. When close to the obstacle pull up to clear the obstacle and if required, smoothly reapply flaps to compensate for decaying airspeed. Immediately lower the nose once clear of the obstacle and slowly retract any flaps.

18. Short field obstacle take-off. Once clear of the trees, the nose is immediately lowered and flaps slowly retracted.

Short and soft field take-off over an obstacle

Also refer to section on unimproved soft and rough surfaces (Off airport landing sites) on page 49.

Apply optimum lift flap. Apply full power on the brakes and ensure that you have maximum static RPM.

Nose wheel airplanes - Release brakes and maintain full back pressure on the stick. When nose rises relax just enough back pressure on the stick to keep the nose wheel off the ground, then apply more flaps and help the aircraft off the ground by adding positive back pressure on the stick or wheel.

Tail wheel airplanes - Allow the tail to rise, but keep it low during the run so as to get weight off the main wheels as soon as possible. When the airplane is ready to fly, apply more flap and positive back pressure on the stick or wheel.

Immediately lower the nose in ground effect and retract as much flap as soon as possible in order to lose drag and accelerate. Remain in ground effect to build as much speed as possible. When close to the obstacle apply flaps and pull up to clear the obstacle. Immediately lower the nose once clear of the obstacle and smoothly retract flaps.

Crosswind take-off *(see photo 17)*

Set flaps to optimum lift flap setting. Deflect the ailerons fully into the wind during the take-off.

Your flaps and ailerons on the one wing will both be at approximately 10-12°, effectively giving you a massive amount of lift flap on the wing opposite to the crosswind side. This will enable a much shorter ground roll and at the same time one wing low towards the crosswind and so enabling the aircraft to stay on the centreline during the take-off roll.

After lift-off, maintain ground effect for a short while in order to increase the climb out speed.

Once out of ground effect and clear of obstacles along the side of the airstrip, if possible, turn the airplane into the wind to continue the climb.

19. Demonstrating an extreme cross wind take-off,

maintaining the runway centreline with the rudder.

LANDINGS

Optimum Performance Landing

An "Optimum Performance Landing" is simply the landing at the end of a "Stabilized Approach". Maintain the Optimum Stabilized Approach Speed all the way down into ground effect, then flare, reduce or cut the power and hold off by continuing to raise the nose. Provided you're at the Optimum Stabilized Approach Speed you will not float very far and if you have sufficient weight in the rear of the airplane you should have a smooth positive nose up touch down on the main wheels. Maintain full back pressure on the stick or control wheel until coming to a full stop.

Short Field Landing

Set up a stabilized, slightly nose low initial approach with flaps and maintain just sufficient speed to keep the nose of the aircraft aimed just before the touchdown spot. Don't ever let the attitude become flat or "drag it in" unnecessarily too early into the final approach. This could be very dangerous, as you may get to far behind the drag curve and not have sufficient power to stop the aircraft from sinking towards the ground, possibly resulting in a full power and full flap stall!

On short final apply full flap and allow the speed to drop down to just above the airspeed that allows the aircraft to start sinking. You will now be at a low speed with a high power setting and a slightly higher nose attitude, known as "on the drag curve". At this time ensure you are alert and ready on the throttle in the event of a sudden sink! You don't want to touch down prior to the usable landing area.

Maintain this configuration all the way down into ground effect and until just before the touchdown spot. Plan to be at the touchdown spot as low as possible above the ground (3ft/1m) at the lowest possible speed.

At the touchdown spot cut the power and flare as the airplane sinks. If the airplane wants to balloon or float then you are going too fast. In such a case immediately, but smoothly retract flaps as required to get the airplane to sink towards the ground whilst pulling back on the stick / control wheel at the same time.

As the aircraft touches down, retract all the flaps and apply hard braking, keeping the stick fully back until the aircraft comes to a full stop. Be careful not to lock up the brakes.

Short Field "Spot" Landing (Ground Effect Landing)

The absolute extreme short field landing!

As previously described under "Ground Effect", an extreme short field "Ground Effect Spot Landing" is achieved when conditions permit the airplane to be able to descend into ground effect prior to the threshold or touch down spot.

The following approach technique is the same as used to set up the Stabilized Approach.

Aiming point

Firstly a stabilized approach must be set up with a slightly higher than normal glide slope. The nose of the aircraft or the "Gun Sight" on the windshield must be locked on to the aiming point until almost in ground effect. The aiming point is the point where the airplane would impact the airstrip or runway, if the pilot did not round-out into a flare.

20. Short field landing in a confined space.

21. Gravel bar on the side of a river.

Touchdown spot

This is the spot where you want the main wheels of the airplane to touch down and is roughly about 50-100m / 150-300ft after the aiming point.

Set up a stabilized approach with full flaps and use pitch and power to maintain just sufficient speed to keep the nose of the aircraft aimed at the "aiming point".

On short final apply slight brake pressure and power as required. If the aircraft starts sinking too rapidly, smoothly apply just sufficient power to reduce the sink only.

Maintain this configuration down into ground effect, then raise the nose as much as possible in order to slow the airplane down to just above the power on stall speed and smoothly apply sufficient power only to keep the airplane flying about 3ft/1m above the surface. (You will be well behind the "drag curve" with the stall warning blaring away and possibly at zero indicated airspeed). It is important to note that the aircraft will only be able to land in a nose high attitude, if you have sufficient weight or ballast at the rear of the plane. In other words, provided it is not "nose heavy".

As soon as you arrive at the touch down spot, cut the power and the aircraft should immediately stall onto the ground in an already nose high attitude without any further flaring, floating or hold-off.

Alternatively you can leave the power setting as is, retract the flaps and simultaneously apply more pitch up, if not already at full stick back. (With manual flaps, this technique is almost similar to landing a helicopter).

Immediately upon touch down apply hard braking holding the stick fully back until the aircraft comes to a full stop. Regardless to the technique or combination of techniques used at the touchdown spot there will be no flaring or floating and if you have misjudged your height above the ground at this time, you may experience a hard landing.

Short and soft field landing

Also refer to section on unimproved soft and rough surfaces (Off airport landing sites) on page 49.

Use the same techniques as mentioned in "Short Field Landing" with the exception that after the aircraft touches down retract only partial flaps and apply moderate braking whilst keeping the stick fully back until the aircraft comes to a full stop. In a tail dragger on very soft sand the tail may want to rise due to the main wheels digging in under hard braking. Simply reduce brake pressure. In some severe cases a small amount of power may be required to keep the tail down.

When attempting to turn a nose wheel airplane around in very soft sand use a reasonable forward speed, full back pressure on the stick and apply lots of power through the turn. Straighten out, line up, run forward a short distance, cut the power and apply light braking if required.

Short Field Landing over obstacles

22. Short final approach over and between obstacles.

24. Touchdown , cut remaining power and retract flaps.

Use this technique for both nose wheel and tail wheel aircraft.

23. Once clear of the obstacles, reduce power & flare for the touchdown spot.

25. Stick fully back with hard braking to a full stop.

Short Field Landing over an obstacle *(see photos 20-23)*

Set up a stabilized final approach with flaps as required and use power to maintain just sufficient speed to keep the nose of the aircraft aimed at the obstacle.

On short final apply full flaps. Do not allow the aircraft to sink lower than the obstacle ahead of you at any time! This is very dangerous, especially when operating near the drag curve.

Once clear of the obstacle, immediately lower the nose, reduce or adjust power as necessary and aim for the touchdown spot. It may be necessary to slip if you don't want to waste too much usable landing area. Your speed should be only just above the stall or else you may float during the round-out.

Just prior to touch down apply power as required just to help raise the nose some more to cushion the landing. If the aircraft wants to balloon or float then retract flaps.

Another more radical technique resulting in an even shorter landing is to, once clear of the obstacle, reduce the power to allow the airplane to descend in an almost flat attitude just on the stall assisted with a small amount of power as required. On entering ground effect apply a larger amount of power and raise the nose to cushion the touchdown. This technique should only ever be attempted by a highly skilled bush pilot and even then it is still a high risk maneuver. Some new experimental bushplanes are equipped with special shock absorbing landing gear to absorb the rebound.

As the aircraft touches down, retract all the flaps and apply hard braking keeping the stick fully back until the aircraft comes to a full stop.

Crosswind landings *(see photo 24)*

Under normal conditions on a normal runway, the usual technique is to crab it in with partial flaps, then on very short final put one wing down into the wind and land with partial flap and possibly on the upwind main wheel first. As the airplane decelerates the control surfaces in the order of rudder, elevator and then ailerons start losing effectiveness. Continue to add more aileron into the wind until the opposite main wheel touches the ground. Maintain full aileron into the wind whilst keeping the airplane straight with rudder and power.

When landing on a short and narrow bush strip, the "norm" is not always possible an may require more advanced techniques. During a gusting crosswind on a short narrow one-way-in bush strip apply full flap on short final approach with a slightly higher than normal speed and with the airplane aimed straight down the centre holding one wing low into the crosswind.

At touchdown retract all the flaps and hold the stick fully back under braking. The airplane should touchdown on the low wing main wheel first then the opposite wheel and nose or tail wheel. In severe cross wind conditions power will be needed in addition to rudder and differential braking to control the aircraft and prevent a ground loop.

26. Demonstrating an extreme crosswind landing.

Dogleg strips and winding roads

When planning to land on a dogleg strip or the bend of a road, try touchdown as early and as far ahead of the kink or bend as possible. This will allow the aircraft space to slow down, enabling it to make the turn without too much skidding.

Alternatively, if this is not possible, plan the touchdown at the beginning of the bend in a banked turn landing on one main wheel first.

Holding the airplane in the bank until the road straightens, then cut the power allowing the opposite main wheel, then nose or tail wheel to touch down.

This technique is also used when landing on a straight strip that has very high ground or obstacles on the final approach, forcing you to approach at an angle and land in a turn.

Uphill / downhill strips

It is always better to land uphill and take-off down hill even with a slight tailwind. A short downhill runway would in effect be much longer than it really is for take-off.

A simple rule of thumb can be used to calculate the runway gradient: every 1.0° grade equals approximately 10% change in effective runway length. Refer to the POH using the density altitude and winds to calculate take-off distance.

To calculate the effective runway length simply measure the elevation of the runway at the top and bottom, then subtract the lower from the higher and divide by the length to find the gradient.

Example:

Runway Length: 600m x 3 = 1800ft

High end: 4900ft
Low end: 4825ft
= 75 ft difference
75 x 100 = 7500
7500 ÷ 1800 = 4°

1800ft (600m) runway length = 4° slope x 10 = 40% increase in runway length if taking off downhill or landing uphill. Effectively you now have an 840m runway.

Landing uphill on very steep strips requires a high power setting during the flare. Depending on the gradient, the final part of approach may need to be made in level flight or even a climb.

Keeping a little power on helps to prevent the aircraft from a premature touchdown and the propeller wash assists in keeping the nose up during the flare. The steeper the uphill, the more power will be required to keep the nose high to prevent the aircraft from landing "flat" or the nose wheel from touching down first.

Rule of thumb:
- Down-slope take-off distance is reduced by about 5% per degree of slope.
- Up-slope take-off distance is increased by about 7% per degree of slope.

Landing on water *(With wheels)*

Occasionally, if landing on a very short beach or island area, it may be necessary to utilize the ground effect over the water to help slow the plane down and in extreme cases actually touch down on the water prior to the dry landing area. Also during heavy rain you sometimes may need to land on a slightly flooded area with shallow water.

Part of this technique is also known as "Water Skiing". However, water skiing can only be done safely in a tail dragger and at a wheeler landing speed. It is not wise to attempt water skiing with a tricycle gear "nose wheel" aircraft.

If you intend to land in shallow water your aircraft should be fitted with raised gear and high floatation tyres, then water depth should be no more than about a third of the diameter of the wheels. You must also consider the propeller tip to water surface clearance. Always load sufficient weight or ballast in the rear of the airplane.

A nose wheel airplane must always be flown onto the water in a nose high attitude with full flaps and power on at the slowest possible speed above stall, in other words "Hanging on the Prop". A tail dragger may be flown gently onto the water surface at an approach speed in a "wheeler" landing configuration with full flaps whilst maintaining sufficient speed and a slight forward stick position to keep the wheels skimming across the or skiing on the surface until reaching shallow water or land.

When reducing the power and as the wheels sink into the water, keep the stick fully back and sufficient power on until the wheels make contact with the ground under the water and the airplane has slowed down to taxi speed. You will require a high power setting to keep the airplane moving through the water. Do not cut the power during taxi unless you want to bring the airplane to a full stop. Cutting the power during taxi may result in the airplane's wheels getting stuck in mud, rocks or roots.

27 & 28. Demonstrating the water skiing technique.

29. A water assisted landing onto a gravel bar.

Author landing the C172 on a flooded marsh

30. Touchdown . (8:50x10 main tires & 8:00x6 nose tire).

31. Main wheels skiing on surface of the water.

32. Abrupt slowing down as nose wheel sinks into water.

Taking off or landing with a tailwind

A rule of thumb: Every 10% increase in ground speed will require a 20% increase in runway length. Normally landings are always made uphill and take-offs downhill, even if there is a small amount of tailwind.

Gross weight

When flying in and out of short strips, fly with as little weight as possible, but don't sacrifice fuel, water or survival equipment.

Rule of thumb: A 10% increase in the take-off gross weight will require a 5% increase in the take-off speed, 10% decrease in acceleration to take-off speed, and 20% increase in the take-off distance.

Density altitude

Density altitude is a major contributing factor towards many aircraft accidents in Africa. It is even more dangerous for pilots that have spent most of their time flying at low elevations such as coastal areas and then one day find themselves having to take-off from an airstrip or airfield at 5000ft above sea level on a hot summer's day. Many pilots that live and fly along the coastal areas rarely think about density altitude as they may never before have experienced any scary take-offs due to a high density altitude situation.

Regardless to what the aircraft operating handbook says about the "service ceiling", most normally aspirated light aircraft do not climb well above 8000ft asl. An airfield on the South African Highveld at about 5000ft elevation above sea level on a hot 35° summer's day will have a density altitude of over 8000ft. Regardless of how long the runway is, you may just find yourself sinking towards the trees off the far end of the runway after take-off.

Always be aware of the density altitude of the airfield or area that you plan to take-off from. Especially if at gross weight on a short strip at a high elevation.

For each 10° F above (or below) standard temperature add (or subtract) 600 feet to (from) the airfield's elevation.

With every 1000ft above sea level the take-off run will increase by approximately 10%. A 10% increase in gross weight equals 20% increase in take-off distance.

Normally aspirated aircraft engines (i.e. non turbo) lose approximately 3% horsepower per every 1000ft above sea level, i.e. 30% horse power at 10 000ft asl.

For each 1000ft asl. true airspeed during landing will increase by approximately 2% (indicated airspeed will remain the same), resulting in a longer landing roll.

Density altitude "Hot and High" take-off

A "Hot & High" take-off is a departure from an airfield or strip at a high elevation on a hot day.

During such conditions it is best to use the optimum performance take-off or even a mild short field take-off technique to get the aircraft off the ground as early as possible. By doing this you will reduce friction and drag. After take-off, hold the aircraft in ground effect so as to quickly accelerate to a safe climb speed.

The worst thing you can do is to keep the aircraft on the runway in order to obtain a higher than normal rotation speed. This is a very dangerous mistake made by many pilots which has resulted in many serious and fatal accidents. All you achieve by doing this is using up the runway and valuable ground effect.

By using a short field or optimum take-off technique and then keeping the aircraft in ground effect to accelerate, you should obtain a higher airspeed at the same position over the runway that you would have had if you had kept the wheels on the runway.

Density altitude computation table

The following table is very easy and quick to use. It is not necessary to know the elevation of where you are in order to calculate the density altitude. Simply observe the outside temperature and dial in 29.92" / 1013.2mb on your altimeter and read off the indicated altitude. Using the indicated altitude refer to the table below to calculate the density altitude and then refer to the aircraft POH to determine the required take-off distance.

Remember that the thermometer in the aircraft may be over reading due to its probe baking in the sun. This may be a good thing, adding a safety margin to the calculated density altitude. However remove it if possible and place it in the shade before reading it. If it cannot be removed, then cover it and allow to cool down.

On the following table the scale at the top represents the elevation in feet above sea level of where you are according to your altimeter set at 29.92" / 1013mb. The numbers in the center represent the density altitude with reference to the temperatures indicated in either Centigrade or Farenheight on the left and right side of the table.

Density altitude computation table

The scale at the top represents the elevation in feet above sea level of where you are according to your altimeter set at 29.92" / 1013mb. The numbers in the center represent the density altitude with reference to the temperatures indicated in either Centigrade or Farenheight on the left and right side of the table.

ºC	2000ft	3000ft	4000ft	5000ft	6000ft	7000ft	8000ft	ºF
4	1217	2454	3690	4924	6156	7385	8613	40
7	1549	2784	4017	5248	6477	7704	8929	45
10	1878	3110	4340	5568	6794	8019	9240	50
13	2203	3432	4660	5885	7108	8329	9549	55
16	2524	3751	4975	6198	7418	8637	9853	60
18	2841	4065	5287	6507	7725	8940	10154	65
21	3155	4376	5595	6812	8027	9240	10452	70
24	3465	4683	5900	7114	8327	9537	10746	75
27	3771	4987	6201	7413	8622	9830	11036	80
29	4074	5287	6498	7708	8915	10120	11323	85
32	4373	5584	6793	7999	9204	10407	11608	90
35	4669	5878	7084	8288	9490	10690	11888	95
38	4962	6168	7371	8573	9773	10971	12166	100
41	5252	6455	7656	8855	10053	11248	12441	105
43	5538	6739	7938	9134	10329	11522	12713	110
46	5822	7020	8216	9411	10603	11793	12982	115
49	6102	7298	8492	9684	10874	12062	13248	120
52	6380	7573	8765	9954	11142	12327	13511	125

CHAPTER 2

MOUNTAIN FLYING

33.

MOUNTAIN FLYING

Introduction

A pilot's first experience of flying over or near mountainous areas could be an overwhelming, intimidating and frightening experience if they have never been exposed to this environment before, especially if the pilot has only ever flown over flatlands and never received any basic training or briefing on mountain flying.

Being frightened by or having a fear of flying in the mountains is a result of a pilots lack of knowledge, awareness and experience. This is very unhealthy as this fear can easily lead to a dangerous situation caused by the pilot not knowing how to deal with a typical mountain flying situation. Mountain flying knowledge and experience will replace the fear with awareness and skill. If you experience fear when flying near mountains then I highly recommend that you stay away at a safe altitude and distance until you have received some basic mountain flying training by a suitably qualified person experienced in mountain flying.

Flying in mountainous areas is vastly different to flatlands and especially sea level flatlands. Flat level areas for forced landings are virtually non-existent in the mountains, abrupt changes in horizontal and vertical wind directions and velocity can occur as well as severe turbulence, downdrafts, rotor winds and updrafts which are very common during windy conditions. The air at mountain elevations is thinner (less dense) resulting in a loss of lift of the wings, propeller thrust and engine power, and this situation is worsened by a rise in temperature (Density Altitude).

Flying in the mountains often results in the aircraft frequently being operated in close proximity to the side of a mountain and rising terrain. Unlike airstrips on flatlands, the majority of mountain strips are sloped "one-way-in-one-way-out", therefore the pilot does not have a choice of take-off or landing direction or a go-around. Operating in the mountains offers a much smaller margin for error.

Mountain flying can be very pleasurable and safe, provided the pilot has proper training by a suitably qualified person experienced in mountain flying and furthermore does proper flight planning prior to flying in this environment. Although there are many flight schools nestled in or around mountainous areas they may not have a suitably qualified instructor experienced in mountain flying.

Mountain flying rules

The following rules must always be adhered to when operating in a mountainous area:

- Don't go if the weather is bad, especially if clouds are obscuring the mountain tops.
- Always know what the wind direction is, so that you don't fly into a downdraft or severe turbulence.
- If you don't know what the wind direction is, you must determine the wind direction as soon as possible by using the turbulence and visualization method.
- Maintain situational awareness at all times. Be continuously aware of your aircraft direction and the direction of the wind with regards to the compass.
- When operating low level in confined spaces, always slow the airplane down to within the white arc and apply flaps. This will allow you to "stay ahead of the aircraft" and

situation and to instantly perform a canyon turn. Lower the gear, if flying a high performance retractable gear aircraft.

- Never fly in the middle of a canyon or gorge. You may not have sufficient room to turn around and even if you do, you may fly into the downdraft side of the canyon as well as possibly being subjected to shear turbulence in the middle.

- Always fly close to the up-draft side of a canyon.

- Always remain in a position from where you can easily and safely turn to lowering terrain.

- Never place the aircraft in any position that could possibly lead to a crash.

- Always cross a ridge at a 45-degree angle so that you are able to escape away from it in the event of been unable to clear the top due to turbulence or down-drafts.

- If inadvertently flying into a down-draft apply full power, lower the nose and turn away in the opposite direction. Never slow down or try out-climb a down-draft.

- Always try to choose routes that offer suitable forced or precautionary landing sites.

- Always ensure you have sufficient fuel, water, first-aid and survival equipment.

- Use the same indicated airspeed for take-off and landing, whether at sea level or at a high elevation mountain strip.

- Use your "6th" sense". If you experience anxiety ("bad feeling"), then immediately turn back or abort.

34. When flying in a narrow gorge or canyon, always fly as close as possible to one side. In windy conditions, always fly on the updraft side.

Mountain flying rules of thumb

- Determining true airspeed: Add 2% to your indicated airspeed for every 1000ft above sea level.
- Increased take-off distance at high altitudes: Take-off run will increase approximately 12% for every 1000ft above sea level.
- Increase in landing speed at high altitudes: Ground speed will increase by approximately 2% for every 1000ft above sea level. However you should use the same indicated airspeed that you would use at sea level.
- To remain clear of turbulence over a mountain range during high winds of 20 knots or more, fly at an altitude above the mountain equal to at least half the height of the mountain above the surrounding terrain over where you are flying.

High elevations

Whenever possible, plan all flights for early morning or late afternoon, especially in the summer months. Density altitude is lower during the cooler, early parts of the day. Heavy convection turbulence can be encountered during midday.

High elevations, high temperature and gusting winds are a deadly combination.

Wind and turbulence

Always be aware of the wind direction over the tops of mountains as well as between them. If flying over the top of mountains in very windy conditions, try to fly 1000ft over the tops so that you are not affected by the severe turbulence of rotor winds. Low level winds between mountains may differ in direction within a few miles radius.

Mountain waves

Mountain waves form over the top of a mountain range. They are caused by high winds flowing within 30° perpendicular to the mountain range with a velocity of 20 knots or more near the top of the mountains increasing in velocity with altitude. The waves downwind from the mountain are "standing waves" or "lee waves." You can expect severe rotor winds under these waves.

The presence of mountain waves are sometimes indicated by lenticular clouds. Look out for rotor clouds on the lee side, they will warn you that severe turbulent rotor winds exist on that side of the mountain. If the lenticular cloud has a rough or ragged shape, then it could contain the same turbulence as the rotor area.

However, clouds are not always present to act as a visual warning of possible severe turbulent conditions ahead, so you should always try to get a weather report prior to crossing a mountain range or you may encounter Clear Air Turbulence (CAT). Refer to your ground speed for an indication of the wind direction, velocity and position of possible down-drafts and rotors.

To remain clear of severe turbulence, attempt to fly at a height of about 50% the height of the mountain above the surrounding terrain. Remember that this is only a rule of thumb and you may need to climb even higher during extreme cases. For example: If the elevation of the terrain that you flying over is 2000ft asl and the mountain top you are attempting to cross is 7000ft asl (5000ft agl), you will need to climb to at least 9500ft asl to be clear of severe turbulence *(see figure 1).*

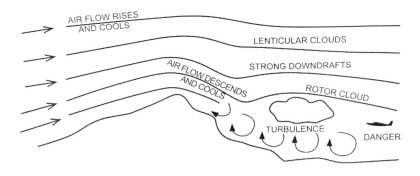

Figure 1. Mountain Waves

Determining wind direction *(see figure 3)*

An easy way to determine the low level wind direction over a mountainous area is to fly close to the one side near the top of high ground or a ridge. If you experience turbulence the wind is probably coming from the opposite side of the high ground (windward side). You are now flying on the leeward side. Cross over to the high ground on the opposite side of the valley or canyon, if the conditions are less turbulent and you experience lift here, draw an imaginary vector between the turbulent side and the more stable and smoother side. The wind will be blowing from the turbulent side towards the side that offers more stable conditions and lift. You have now determined the approximate wind direction in the area that you are flying. After a short while flying over and along the side of hills, peaks and ridges you should be able to determine the actual direction of the wind with fair accuracy.

The subject of turbulence is mentioned frequently further on in this chapter as it is a common hazard in mountainous areas.

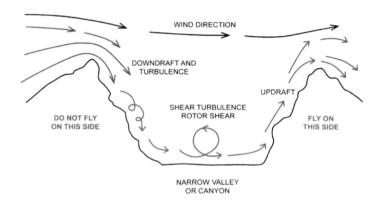

Figure 2. Downdrafts and updrafts.

Downdrafts and updrafts *(see figure 2)*

Always be aware of where the downdrafts and updrafts are. Pay attention to turbulence as well as to your VSI and ASI.

If caught in a downdraft, fly "downhill" and "surf it out", do not try to out climb it. Hills and mountains covered by forests can absorb a lot of the downdraft so when flying low you could actually be pushed down into the trees instead of benefiting from an expected up-draft or cushion effect as in the case of flying low over high ground without forests away from the down-draft.

Never fly in the middle of a narrow valley or canyon for two main reasons. 1. You must always ensure that you have sufficient space to turn around safely and without flying into a downdraft. 2. Rotor shear may exist in the centre. If possible always keep to the side that has the least turbulence and no downdraft or "rotor winds". Fly along the side that offers smoother conditions and updraft. If you encounter a downdraft or severe turbulence, immediately turn away and fly towards the opposite "downwind" side.

Do not get confused between the terms "downwind" and "downdraft" or "upwind" and "updraft". These are completely different. The terms "downwind" and "upwind" refer to the aircraft's position in relation to the wind, whilst the terms "downdraft" and "updraft" refer to the direction of the wind up or down the face of a mountain. Rotor winds are normally encountered during the "downdraft".

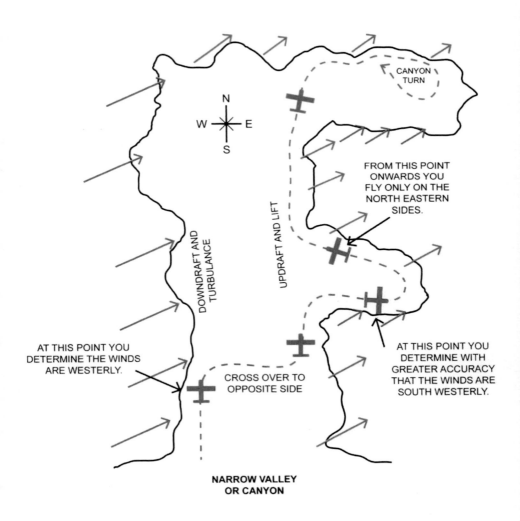

Figure 3. Determining wind direction from downdrafts and updrafts. In this example, the winds are south westerly.

Mountain breeze

A mountain breeze is a wind that blows downstream in the evening. It is caused by the air descending down the mountain face as it cools down after sunset *(see figure 4)*.

Valley breeze

A valley breeze is a wind that blows upstream in the morning. It is caused by the sun's rays heating the ground in the valley *(see figure 5)*.

Anabatic breeze

Even without any wind blowing over a mountain one can still encounter down- and updrafts. This is caused by the sun's heating of the surface on the one side of a valley whilst the opposite surface is in the sun's shadow. The surface that receives the sun's rays will produce rising convection currents known as "anabatic lift" whilst the opposite surface may have a mild downdraft *(see figure 6)*.

Mountain ridges

Always approach a ridge or pass at a 45° angle so that you can easily and quickly make a 90° turn towards lower ground in case you encounter severe turbulence and downdraft. Never cross a ridge at a 90° angle if flying at or below the height of the ridge.

False horizon

Be aware of the horizon when flying over or towards mountains. A gentle upslope terrain may create the illusion of a higher horizon and thus cause a constant climb. Remember that the horizon is near the base on the opposite side of the mountains and NOT on top of the mountain!

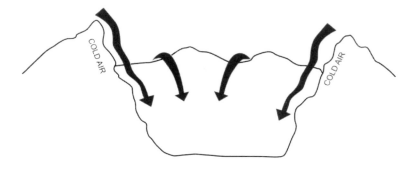

Figure 4. Mountain breeze.

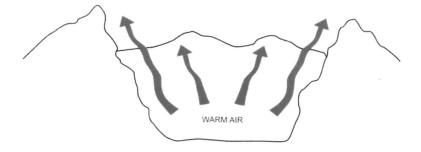

Figure 5. Valley breeze.

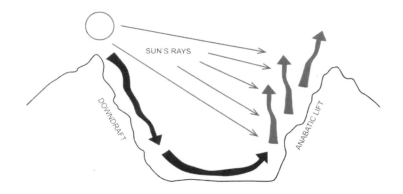

Figure 6. Anabatic breeze.

A useful and practical tool to assist you in learning how to overcome this illusion is to take a short 150-200mm piece of 12mm aluminium or plastic tube and glue a spirit level head onto the middle of it. When in doubt about whether or not you may make it over the mountain in front of you, simply hold it up, center the bubble and look through it. If you can see over the mountain ahead then you will make it over the top so that there is no need to climb before getting to the mountain.

Weather reports

Always try to find out what the weather is like on the other side of the mountains before commencing the flight.

Flight planning

If not filing a flight plan then at least tell someone where you are flying to, your planned routing and what time you expect to return or arrive at your destination. If possible, be in contact with an area control or ATC. Whenever possible, plan your route so that you fly over well known or popular passes, roads, gorges and valleys.

Sunset

Allow for an extra half hour of daylight if flying to a low lying strip in a valley or canyon without runway lighting. There may be plenty of daylight at cruise altitude, but it may already be dark at the destination airfield because of shadows from the surrounding mountains.

Night and IFR flying in mountainous areas

Night vision

Prior to a night flight take in a lot of vitamin A. This can be via a vitamin supplement or even just the old fashion way, carrots and dairy products. Night vision is highly dependent on Vitamin A.

Avoid bright white light prior to or during a night flight. The human eye takes up to 30 minutes to fully adapt t

o the dark, however, this can be lost immediately if exposed to any bright light.

Take-off and departure

Prior to departing from an airstrip at night familiarize yourself with the surrounding terrain and obstacles and have a departure plan in mind.

After take-off maintain a positive angle of climb by referring to the airspeed indicator rather than using the artificial horizon for attitude. Acceleration error in the AH during the climb may indicate a false, higher than normal nose high attitude. This could result in the pilot lowering the nose and flying into terrain or obstacles.

If you are unsure of the proximity of terrain in the immediate area or become disorientated, locate a light on the ground and fly towards it, however, be aware of your position from the departure airfield. If the light flickers and/or disappears, there may be terrain between you and the light source (or an electrical failure). Immediately turn 180° away from it and fly back towards your point of departure. Even if the light stays constant you must still turn back 180° over the light, as you may not know if there is high ground or obstacles further on. Performing a teardrop turn will keep the aircraft in a much smaller area.

You should now be flying towards a light or the runway lights at your departure point. Continue this procedure until you have gained sufficient altitude to clear the highest terrain in the area under your intended route from your departure point.

En-route

When flying at night and/or under IFR over mountainous areas, it is advisable to add at least 1000ft to your MEA due to possible altimeter (QNH) errors, especially if you cannot see the ground.

High winds over or between mountains, narrow valleys, gorges and canyons etc. can cause the low level pressure to drop quite dramatically due to the venturi effect of the wind passing over or through these areas.

Radio

Remember that you may not have any radio contact once your are in the mountains. Select a Flight Information Region (FIR), Approach or Information frequency that you know is fairly busy and frequently used by higher flying aircraft overhead in that region. The VHF emergency frequency 121.5mhz may also be used; if your aircraft is equipped with a High Frequency (HF) radio, the emergency frequency is 2182khz. An HF radio has far greater range at low altitudes than a VHF radio. Always carry a frequency chart in the aircraft.

Emergency landing sites

Be continuously aware of possible emergency landing sites and ways out towards lower ground in case of changing weather or engine problems.

Aircraft

Make sure that you are familiar with the airplane you are flying and the POH. Do not attempt flying in the mountains with an aircraft that you are not yet fully familiar with. First get to know how the aircraft handles various maneuvers such as steep turns, slow flight and various configurations of stalls, including incipient spins.

Safety

Stay alert at all times, monitor your fuel and engine instruments frequently, but keep your "head out of the cockpit". It's not a good idea to go mountain flying after a late night of drinking!

Bad weather mountain flying ("Scud Running"*)*

Every year there are many of bad weather mountain flying fatalities caused by "continued VFR flight into adverse weather conditions" resulting in "controlled flight into terrain" (CFIT). Most of these fatal accidents have been with commercial instrument rated pilots flying high performance aircraft. They could have been prevented, if the pilots had at least some form of mountain flying training or experience and used and adhered strictly to the basic mountain flying rules and the following procedures and techniques.

"Scud Running" is not necessarily illegal or unsafe, provided the entire flight can be conducted under VFR and by an experienced mountain pilot. "Scud Running" safely requires a completely different set of procedures and techniques.

If you are unfamiliar with any area en-route, attempt to get as much advise from local pilots that are experienced and familiar with flying in such conditions in those areas. Despite that, use careful judgement and "6th sense" as you could also get bad advice.

If ever you decide to fly in bad weather in a mountainous area then you should at least have some low level mountain flying experience or training. It is almost suicide to attempt to fly low level in a mountainous area during low cloud and marginal visibility if you have never had any low level and mountain flying training! In addition you should preferably be familiar with the area, consider all options and possibilities and, most important at all times, be well ahead of the aircraft and possible scenarios.

Carry an up to date map. Modern moving map, GPS, showing virtual terrain and obstacles is an advantage, however, do not solely rely on this, use it only as additional reference and aid. You must keep your head outside the cockpit and keep the real surrounding terrain and obstacles visual at all times.

When flying between mountains, through a gorge, canyon or narrow valley during overcast or bad weather always be sure your "back door" is open in case you need to turn back. If the weather conditions in the area you are flying through are deteriorating, you must turn back or land.

Also, as mentioned a few more times in this book and of extreme importance, always fly slow (white arc). This will allow you to fly with or apply flaps at any time prior to executing a turn and stay ahead of the aircraft and situation by allowing you more time to look out, think, make decisions and react. Fly as close as possible to the one side so that you have sufficient room to turn around.

Do not fly close to the cloud base as the visibility will be reduced, creating a very high risk of flying into the cloud or a mountain side before you have time to take evasive action. Flying low is far safer and will offer much better forward visibility. Fly at half the hight between the ground and the cloud base or lower. Nevertheless, the lower you fly, the higher the risk of encountering obstacles such as power lines.

Try to follow and fly on the right hand side of main roads or railway tracks as they normally go over the lowest part of a mountain range. Be aware of the possibility of tunnels.

Do not attempt to cross over a saddle, pass or ridge unless you can clearly see VMC conditions ahead.

Turn on all the aircraft lights just in case there's another aircraft flying in the opposite direction.

Even if you are an IF rated pilot, NEVER attempt to climb through cloud to "VFR on Top" in a mountainous area.

If flying with another aircraft, never fly in formation. Decide who is going to be the leader or scout and keep a safe distance behind the lead aircraft at all times. The pilot of the rear aircraft should be a second set of eyes and not just simply follow the leader.

Finally, if at any time you feel unsafe, unsure or get a anxiety feeling ("bad feeling"), turn back and land!

35. "Scud running" bad weather in a mountainous area.

Low flying

Do not fly low level in a canyon or valley towards high ground or upstream if you do not have enough space and low ground to turn around safely.

When only a few feet above the ground and faced with obstacles, use rudder to turn (skidding turns), so as not to allow the wing to get too low. Do not attempt this maneuver with a too low airspeed.

Look out for overhead high tension electrical transmission cables. These often span across gorges, canyons and valleys. These wires are often invisible to the eye so always look out for the pylons first then find the wires between them. Fly close to the pylons as the wires are higher, but be aware that some pylons have support cables. In the event that you are taken by surprise and only see the wires ahead and above you at the last moment, it is better not to pull up! Go straight under the power lines because by the time you see them you may not be able to clear them by pulling up, especially the thinner earth wires higher up. It is safer to fly under as there is usually sufficient space, especially if you are closer to the pylon (*refer to photo 32*).

Be aware of birds. If in a head on collision with one pull up, as birds usually always dive. In the event of a head on bird strike being inevitable, placing your hands on the windshield may help to prevent the windshield from breaking.

When flying near remote bush camps or lodges be on the lookout for high antennas and lightning arresting poles.

36. Flying under high tension power lines.

37. At this abort point, the aircraft can safely turn away towards lower ground to the left.

38. Approaching rising terrain and the "point of no return".

Point of no return/abort point.

There are two different types of "points of no return".

The first is also known as the "abort point" and is the position of the aircraft when approaching to land at a one-way-in-one-way-out mountain strip surrounded by high terrain. At this pre-established point you can still abort the landing and turn away from the high ground towards lower ground and climb away. NEVER fly beyond this point of no return unless you are 100% sure that you are in a position to make a good landing. Once you have passed the abort point the name changes to "point of no return".

The second is the position of the aircraft flying towards up-sloping / rising terrain where, if you reduce the throttle to idle and begin a normal glide, you will have sufficient altitude to either turn around or away from the high ground towards lower ground without impacting the terrain. NEVER fly beyond this point of no return. It takes practice to establish the minimum altitude for this point.

Landing

When approaching to land at a mountain strip, slow down to below flap extension speed and apply 10-20° of flap. Circle the field no higher than 1000 feet and as close as possible to the surrounding mountain sides to check wind direction. As explained earlier under "Wind and turbulence" this is achieved by feeling for turbulence or downdrafts and updrafts and then drawing an imaginary wind vector between the downdrafts and updrafts. The wind will always be blowing from the downdraft and turbulent side towards the updraft and more stable side. Also check the tree tops and grass for signs of wind direction and velocity.

Check the strip for animals, surface condition and obstacles on approach, take note of the terrain surrounding the circuit, approach and departure paths. Decide how you are going to approach and land and choose an "abort point" or "go-around point" in the event that you are too high or fast. Your abort route should always be towards flat or low ground. Most mountain strips are one-way-in-and-one-way-out, so once you are committed you will not be able to do a "go-around".

Maintain a "tight" pattern and keep the airstrip within sight and within gliding distance.

When the landing area is long enough for a normal landing, fly a power assisted stabilized approach with a steep approach angle aiming at or just before the threshold or touchdown spot. The advantage of approaching at a steeper angle is that you will have better forward visibility to see the runway and obstacles on approach as well as being ahead of the power curve instead of "dragging it in". If you experience an engine failure during a steep approach you should still be in a position to make it to the airstrip or landing area after retracting any drag flap.

Six point check prior to landing on a 1-way-in-1-way-out strip

1. Slow down to white arc speed, lower the landing gear and apply 1st notch of flap. Circle around the landing area to determine the following:
2. Determine the approach end of the strip. Determine the final approach path.
3. Determine the escape route in the event of an aborted landing.
4. Determine the abort point.
5. Determine the take-off and departure route.

39. Landing on a 1-way-in-1-way-out sloped strip with the C170.

40. Landing on a narrow mountain trail with the C172

41. Author landing a Cessna 210 on a short 1-way-in-1-way-out-strip.

Take-off

Before take-off carefully plan your climb out route and emergency action in case of an engine failure. Don't take-off towards higher ground or a mountain into direct sunlight or sunset when the ground ahead of you is in shade. Be very aware of downdrafts and dangerous rotor winds when landing and taking off out of mountain strips.

There may be times that after careful study of the temperature, winds and terrain you may need to wait it out. When taking off from a strip in a narrow valley towards rising terrain always turn towards the updraft side during the climb out so as to enable sufficient space to turn back to the strip or perform a circling climb out. Another advantage is that the updraft could assist by increasing the vertical climb speed.

42. Preparing to take-off from a short 1-way-in-1-way-out mountain strip in a confined area.

Canyon turns

When flying between high mountains, through a gorge or narrow valley NEVER fly in the centre. Always fly as far as possible to one side so that if you have to turn around you will have enough space. Plan all your turns towards lower ground.

Before commencing a turn in a canyon or gorge slow the aircraft down to best glide speed by trading altitude for speed and not by reducing power.

When it is necessary to make turns in a canyon or valley, for example when circling overhead an airstrip, normal medium bank turns should be executed by using 20° flaps. Steeper turns may be necessary in more confined spaces. However, the steeper the turn, the higher the stall speed. In a normal light aircraft flying at a speed of about 70 knots a 180° medium bank turn at 30° can be safely and comfortably executed within 500m/1500 feet.

If it is necessary to make a 180° turn in a very narrow canyon or gorge a much tighter turn may be required. This can safely be executed at a 45° angle of bank with about 20° or half notch of flaps, using sufficient power to maintain a safe speed.

If ever in doubt as to which turn to use then use the following one. A very tight turn can be achieved within a 200m/600ft radius by slowing the airplane down to about 10 knots above the stall speed (as indicated in the aircraft POH for a 60° bank with 20° of flap at gross weight), then applying a 60° angle of bank. However, a very high to full power setting may be required in order to maintain altitude and speed (*refer to photo 39).*

Refer to your aircraft POH for the stall speeds at various bank angles and flap settings. It may be interesting to note that the stall speed in a general aviation light aircraft at 40° bank with 40° flap is similar to level flight with 0° flap.

Narrow canyons

If flying up a very narrow canyon where you clearly may not be able to complete a standard 180° canyon turn within half the width of the canyon, you may need to fly up the downdraft side so that you do not enter a downdraft when coming out of a turn. Instead you will now be turning into an updraft, which is far safer.

43. A canyon turn, using 60° angle of bank with 30° flaps.

The Emergency 180° canyon turn:
the ultimate tight turn!

If you frequently fly low level between high ground, mountains, gorges and in valleys, your should practice and become proficient in this maneuver so that if necessary, you will have the ability to get out of a tight spot at any time. This emergency 180° canyon turn is basically a modified chandelle with flaps.

The best way to practice this is to fly up a runway or road at a safe altitude and when abeam a chosen point or landmark, execute the maneuver. Note: This is an aerobatic maneuver that may result in bank angles of more than 90 degrees. It should not be attempted unless you are familiar with basic aerobatic maneuvers and unusual attitude recovery, unless accompanied by a suitably qualified and experienced pilot.

This is how it's done:

- If possible make a slight turn towards the high ground.
- Apply full power with propeller full fine pitch.
- Pull the nose up to about 45°.
- When speed is in the white arc apply half flaps. Do not apply full flap as this may generate too much drag.
- Immediately turn into a 60-90° angle of bank. If you maintain a 60° bank angle on the artificial horizon you will be at about 90° angle of bank at the apex. If you maintain a 90° bank angle on the artificial horizon you will be over 100° (inverted) at the apex.
- Maintain firm back pressure on the stick allowing the nose to fall through the horizon relaxing bank and pitch angle after passing through the apex of the turn or as required to remain off the stall.
- Reduce the angle of bank towards the 180° position of the turn and don't let the nose drop too far below the horizon.
- Level out, reduce power and slowly retract the flaps.

Once you are pointing 180° from the direction you were originally flying, look down and take note of where you are in relation to the landmark you used as a ground reference. Provided that you executed the manoeuver correctly, you will notice that you still appear to be basically over the top of it and in addition you should have also gained over 100ft in altitude.

44. Demonstrating an emergency canyon turn,
the ultimate tight turn! Entry into this maneuver requires
the nose to be pitched up 35-45° with 20-30° of flaps and
60-90° angle of bank.

CHAPTER 3

EMERGENCIES

Emergencies
Emergency 180° turns in mountainous areas
(Refer also to "emergency canyon turn" on the previous page).

Emergency 180° turn in cloud
The first rule is REMAIN CLEAR OF CLOUDS and in VMC at all times, unless you are instrument rated and proficient in instrument flight (IF) and on an IFR flight.

However, if you inadvertently fly into cloud the following procedure should be followed immediately:

- Slow down to under manoeuvring speed.
- Note the compass and/or DI heading.
- Note the time in minutes and seconds. If you have a stop watch, zero it and press start. If not, then as soon as your clock or watch indicates a minute or half a minute, initiate a standard 15° rate left turn using the Artificial Horizon or the turn & bank indicator. Hold the turn for 60 seconds, then roll out back to level flight.
- Maintain altitude cautiously throughout the turn and level flight by referring to the altimeter VSI and ASI.

Emergency straight and level descent through cloud
Imagine a typical scenario: You are "VFR on top", the sun is setting and you're low on fuel. You shouldn't be there in the first place but you are and you are going down one way or another. You have no other option but to descend. You are not sure of the terrain below the cloud. This is the only procedure that can offer you a good chance of survival:

- Move your seat a little further back than normal and secure your seat and shoulder harness.
- If possible choose a westerly or easterly heading to minimize compass card swings.

- Slow the aircraft down to about 10 knots above stall speed and fully extend flaps and landing gear.

- Reduce the power to enable a 500ft per minute descent and a slow forward airspeed.

- Adjust the mixture for a smooth engine operation.

- Adjust all trim tabs for a stabilized hands off descent.

- Keep your hands off the control wheel/stick.

- Check Compass or Direction Indicator (DI), Artificial Horizon (AH) and turn & bank indicator movement and make very cautious movements only with the rudder to stop any turns. However, you can leave all controls alone until breaking cloud. The aircraft may go into a slight descending turn, but it will not go into a spiral dive!

- Upon breaking of the clouds, resume normal flight.

- If you happen to make contact with the ground before breaking cloud, your forward and vertical speed should be low enough to offer a very good chance of survival.

Emergency spin descent through cloud

The advantage of this procedure is to prevent the possibility of getting into a spiral dive. It has been successfully used on occasion. Only use this procedure if the aircraft is not fully loaded, approved for spins and you are 100% sure that the cloud base below you is at least 3000ft above ground, that there are no obstacles, that you are using a GPS and are in radio contact with a pilot or controller on the ground directly below you.

Placing the aircraft into a spin:

- Slowly reduce power to idle, set mixture full rich and apply full carburettor heat.
- Slow the aircraft down to just above stall speed and trim the elevator.
- Just above the cloud, pull the stick all the way back and apply full left or right rudder.
- Hold the controls fully in these positions until breaking cloud.
- Stop the direction of spin by applying full opposite rudder and release back pressure on the stick. If you get disorientated then simply let go of all controls.
- Recover and resume normal flight.

The advantage of the above method is that during a spin a non IF rated pilot has a far less chance of getting into a spiral dive or some other dangerous attitudes.

Recovery from a spiral dive

If you encounter a spiral dive whilst in the clouds, then proceed as follows:

- Reduce power to idle.
- Stop the turn by coordinated aileron and rudder control in the opposite direction to the turn and aligning the Artificial Horizon (AH) horizontally with its horizontal reference lines on the instrument and maybe also the top of the instrument panel and / or aligning the little symbolic airplane in the Turn and Bank Coordinator with its horizontal reference line or if, it's and old style Turn and Bank indicator, center the needle and ball.
- Cautiously apply control stick or wheel back pressure to slowly reduce the airspeed. Take care not to overstress the airframe by applying too much back pressure too quickly.

- Adjust the trim tabs to enable a level and stabilized glide and glide speed.
- Keep your hands off the control stick or wheel using ONLY rudder to control the heading until breaking out clear of cloud.

Night emergency descent and forced landing

Never fly at night in the bush or mountains unless you are very familiar with the area, the landing site has acceptable runway lighting and your aircraft landing lights are 100% operational and correctly aligned.

Engine failure on a dark night out in the remote bush or mountains may call for a similar procedure as stated in "emergency descent through cloud" above.

- Attempt to restart engine as per the Pilots Operating Handbook (POH) engine failure checklist.
- Move your seat a little further back than normal and secure your seat belt and shoulder harness.
- At low altitude extend landing gear and full flaps. Slow the aircraft down to the slowest safe airspeed above stall.
- Use pitch to control no more than 500ft per minute descent.
- Adjust all trim tabs for a stabilized descent.
- Keep al turns within 10-15° bank angle.
- Turn on landing and taxi lights.
- Once in sight of ground make small last minute direction changes just to aim the aircraft between obstacles to a landing site.
- Fly the aircraft all the way down then round out and flare as per a normal power off landing.

If you happen to contact ground before being able to maneuver the aircraft into a suitable landing space, your forward and vertical speed should be low enough to offer a very good chance of survival.

45. Author's C172 on a road in South Africa after engine failure.

Forced landing (day)

- Move your seat a little further back than normal and secure your seat and shoulder harness.
- Fly the aircraft all the way down until short final at best glide speed.
- On short final, extend landing gear and full flaps prior to touchdown. (Leave the landing gear up in case of very soft or rutted surface, mud or water.)
- Make small direction changes just to aim the aircraft between obstacles to a landing site.
- Round out and flare as per a normal power off landing! Don't try to stretch the glide.

Use the wings, landing gear and the bottom part of the fuselage to absorb energy. If possible, use any padding available such as camping mattress, sleeping bag, jackets, blankets and pillows.

Energy absorbing materials such as small trees and fences can be used during the landing to dissipate energy.

Returning to runway after engine failure

During one of my courses, we had just taken off from runway 17 at Barberton and were on the climb out with full power and 10 flaps at approximately 200 foot with the runway behind us, when all of a sudden there was a loud bang, the engine lost power and started vibrating badly. I immediately lowered the nose, applied full flaps, made a steep right turn with the intention of attempting to return to the runway and if not, to put it down between the trees below. Fortunately, I managed to land back on the runway safely. After inspecting the engine, we found that one of the crankshaft counterweights had broken off and gone through the side of the engine, taking a complete cylinder with it.

Much has been discussed about such a scenario and the FAA also conducted exhaustive test flights. At the end of the day it is possible, depending on pilot skill and experience.

A straight climb out on the extended centre line offers very little chance of returning to a runway or strip if the airplane is under 500ft, especially during a shallow climb away from the end of the strip.

The best chance of being able to return to the airstrip after take-off is to get into a habit as often as possible to once airborne, turn out as soon as possible into the wind and climb parallel to the strip maintaining just sufficient distance from the strip to allow a 180° turn back onto the strip in the event of an engine failure. (Keep in mind that you may have a tailwind on landing, as you may have to land in the opposite direction to that of your take-off).

Continue past abeam the threshold and at approximately 45° position from the threshold, turn onto a base leg intercepting the centre line at a 90° angle and continue the climb on the opposite downwind side of the strip until you have sufficient height to continue the flight. In the event of an engine failure you would now be in a position to land into the wind in the direction of your take-off.

This technique is not always possible, especially if it's a very short strip with high ground all around or a controlled airport. In such a case all you can do is simply make the best of this procedure.

Turning away from the runway as soon as possible after take-off allows a better chance of being able to return to the runway in the event of an engine failure.

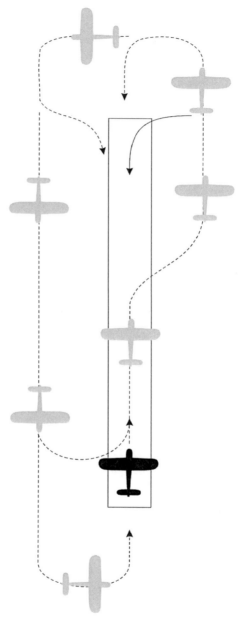

Figure 7. Turning away from runway center line after take-off allows for more chances of returning to the runway in the event of an emergency.

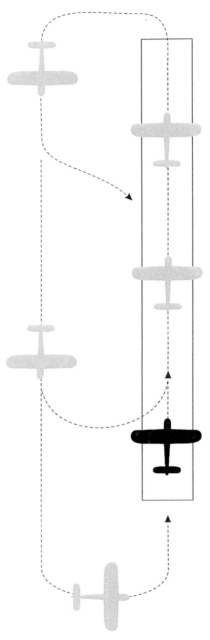

Figure 8. Maintaining runway centre line after take-off offers less chance to return to the runway.

CHAPTER 4

NAVIGATION

NAVIGATION

VFR Low-level navigation & Dead Reckoning (the "Bush Pilot's VOR")

"Dead Reckoning" is the process of estimating your position by advancing a known position using course, speed, time and distance to be travelled. In other words, figuring out where you will be at a certain time if you hold the speed, time and course you plan to travel.

Think about the following scenario: Being in the remote bush where you have no access to weather reports so you do not know what the winds are en-route. You have no operational GPS and you are out of range of any VOR or NDB. Low clouds require you to fly low level over featureless terrain for about 200 miles.

All you need is a chart, an accurate compass, a stopwatch and a "wiz wheel". A simple electronic calculator may be a plus, too.

Start by plotting your course from A to B in the same way you would normally do and determine the magnetic track. Locate as many prominent ground references as possible within visual range of the track and mark them on your chart. In addition write the track distance next to them.

After take-off, position yourself to start your navigation to B by passing overhead the airfield established on the required heading. Start your stopwatch as you pass directly overhead.

Assume your next landmark is 20 nautical miles away and that you are cruising at 100 knots. Distance divided by speed equals the time in a fraction of an hour. To get minutes, multiply this fraction by 60.

Therefore 20 nautical miles divided by 100 knots equal 0.2 of an hour. Multiplying 0.2 by 60 minutes equates to 12 minutes flying time. (20 ÷ 100 = 0.2 and 0.2 x 60min = 12min). If all goes well you should arrive overhead or abeam your first way-point in 12 minutes.

If you only arrive over the waypoint after 15 minutes then you have a head wind. Simply add 3 minutes to your next leg time in case where it is 20 miles long again or 1.5 minutes, should it be a 10 mile leg for instance.

Should you arrive abeam the waypoint on time, but find yourself in some distance, say to the right of it, you have a crosswind from the left. Simply adjust your course a few degrees to the left for the next leg. If you arrive overhead the next waypoint, then apply about half of the previous correction to the heading to the next waypoint, provided that the next waypoint is approximately the same distance away. However, once you have arrived over or abeam a waypoint using this method, it is easy to calculate the wind correction angle using your wiz wheel.

In the event of you missing your waypoint, do not go wandering around looking for it. Stay on your heading and continue to the next point. When conditions such as a crosswind and a lack of ground features create uncertainty as to whether you can arrive overhead your destination, fly a pre-determined amount of degrees off course into wind. When your ETA for destination passes, turn 90° from your track to the opposite side of the crosswind direction and fly straight ahead towards your destination.

Alternatively you can also allow the wind to push you off course and when you arrive at your ETA time turn 90° off your track INTO the wind and fly towards your destination.

Practicing dead reckoning on a regular basis prepares you not only for the eventuality of losing your GPS and other navigation aids, but also polishes your piloting skills to fly accurately. Accurate DR navigation is a skill that could get you home one day when all other methods have failed.

Horizontal visibility and distance

Being able to judge horizontal visibility and distance at any given time without reference to a chart or any electronic aid such as GPS or DME comes with experience. An easy way to hone this skill is to identify where you are on your chart and then pick a town, structure or peak either 5nm or 10nm in the distance. If you can just see this place on the map and no further then that's the visible distance or visibility and distance in nm. If you can see further, then select another place 10 nm in the distance and so on...

If you cannot see a town or structure 5nm away then as soon as you see the town, check the distance using your chart and that will be your visibility.

Night landings at bush strips

If landing at a bush strip at night, you should be familiar with the strip or at least have a proper briefing with another pilot as well as the ground support who know the strip. Adequate runway edge illumination should be available and placed every 100m/330ft either side (i.e. paraffin/kerosine lamps, pit fires or solar LED lights). Some low cost garden walkway solar LED lights can easily be modified to be used as low intensity airstrip lights.

If runway edge lighting is not available, then at least two vehicles must be positioned so that one vehicle is parked just before the threshold with all its head lights on high beams facing the strip so as to illuminate the landing area, the rear tail lights will be facing the approach. The second vehicle should be at the far end of the strip with its tail lights facing the strip and its head lights on high beam so as to illuminate any obstacles at the end of the strip in the event of the aircraft having to do a go-around. In bad visibility both vehicles should have their brake lights on, as well as emergency flashers. If the vehicles are equipped with high intensity rear fog lights then these should also be on. Never face both vehicle head lights towards the landing area as this may confuse the pilot as to which end the approach should be made, as well as cause night blindness during the approach.

Aircraft landing lights should be properly aligned for night landings. Standard aircraft landing lights, although fairly effective on a runway equipped with lights, are usually totally insufficient for landing in the bush at night. There are very effective new technology high intensity spot and flood lights on the market, however, most are not certified for use on aircraft and those that are cost a fortune. When operating at unlighted strips at night I have many times had to clamp large off-road vehicle spot lights to the wing struts or landing gear as the standard aircraft lights were insufficient. When doing this, you should take care not to mount the lights in a position that will cause a reflection off the rear of the propeller, this will create a 'disk' effect that you will not be able to see through at night.

"GPS approaches" into bush strips

You may need to design your own set of GPS "approach plates" due to marginal weather or night conditions out in the bush and the absence of any weather information for the area and at the destination. Please note that I use the word "marginal" and not "IMC"! The following is only a rough guide and should not be used in IMC conditions, ONLY marginal VMC (in sight of ground) or at night.

Most IFR rated pilots should be able to draw up a reasonable GPS approach plate. It's essential to try and have an initial and final approach fix that can be established by using at least one VOR radial, DME as well as GPS co-ordinates. This may however not be possible, especially where high ground or mountains get in the way of a distant VOR signal in which case then at least an NDB radial should be used. Some NDBs can be received over a very long distance, even with higher ground in between.

Another important consideration is the possible absence of barometric pressure information of the area. Your only means of determining height above terrain would be to compare the indicated altitude on your GPS and altimeter set to the nearest barometric pressure, so an extra safety margin should be incorporated especially into the MDA.

Careful planning must go into designing an approach and all obstacles and high ground must be recorded and clearly indicated.
Finally, the approach and missed approach must be properly test flown under CAVOK conditions prior to being used under any marginal weather conditions or at night.

CHAPTER 5

SURVIVAL

46. Survival kit, tools and equipment.

Survival

Part 1. Survival kit, tools and equipment

Always expect and be prepared for the unexpected referring to the saying: Failing to prepare is preparing to fail.

Although the following list looks very exhaustive and heavy, the whole lot (with the exception of some mandatory items such as a fire extinguisher) including 2 persons personal clothing and 10ltr of drinking water only weighs about 80kg/176lbs, the same weight as one average adult person. If you are flying a 2-seater aircraft and are severely limited for space, you will need to sift through this list and decide what items are most important for you. However, I recommend that you never sacrifice water, first aid and some basic survival tools such as a multi-tool and knife.

The following recommendation on aircraft seats is my personal opinion and is to be regarded as a rough guide only. For safety reasons, a single engine four place light airplane with an engine producing less than 230hp flying out into the remote bush should not have any rear seats installed and only carry two adults. This will ensure that there is more than sufficient space and useful weight left over for survival equipment and luggage. A four place airplane with an engine producing 230hp or more should not carry more than three adults plus equipment. However, 4-seater airplanes seldom offer sufficient space to carry three adults plus all the survival equipment and personal luggage. An airplane with an engine producing over 280hp will normally be a six place airplane and should only have a maximum of four seats installed to allow for four adults plus luggage and survival equipment.

The older model 4-seater Cessna 100 series airplanes without the rear window allow for much more room in the rear. The rear partition behind the baggage compartment can easily be removed allowing for a removable floor and new rear panel to be installed over the control cables. This allows for another 3ft/1m of cabin space. During flight all the lightweight bulky stuff such as sleeping bags, mattresses and empty plastic containers etc. can be stored with very little effect on the aft CG. However, always ensure that the CG is maintained well within the envelope. On the ground this allows for two adults to sleep very comfortably without having to remove the two front seats.

Although the temperature may be warm at your point of departure, conditions may not be as warm if you find yourself having to overnight out in a mountainous or desert area even in the middle of summer. Clothing should be warm, comfortable and practical, preferably be 100% cotton or wool. Advisable are a bush jacket and pants with many pockets, including down the side of the legs, also if you are wearing shorts in the hot summer months. A fire retardant flight suit with many pockets and a belt for attaching all your accessories such as multi-pliers, survival knife, flashlight and survival pouch is very useful, too. This may be more comfortable and suitable under certain conditions. Boots should be comfortable and of a good quality, made from real leather. Synthetic materials do not offer good protection against the elements and will melt into your skin in the event of a fire.

I never fly on a cross country flight without specific equipment on board my airplane, as I had to learn by own experience. Once you have been in a situation where you really wish you had brought a certain item with for survival, you will never forget it or regard it as unnecessary again. Depending on the type of flight and where you are going, you may not need to take all this equipment with you, but be very careful as to what you leave behind.

Obviously the larger the aircraft, the less effect all this equipment will have on the weight and balance, but the more crew and passengers, the more survival food and water will need to be carried.

Always ensure that your first aid kit, fire extinguisher, food and water is located close to your seat and the door, so that you can easily grab them after an incident. Next is your personal kit and tools, followed by the rest of the equipment.

Communication and navigation:

- aeronautical paper charts,
- navigation rule and protractor,
- flight computer,
- pens and pencils,
- pocket hiking and plotting compass (to be carried in your pocket),
- hand held GPS and charger
- HF Aviation radio or 'radio ham' set (installed in aeroplane)
- hand held VHF aviation radio with charger,
- cell phone and/or a satellite phone and charger is a big advantage and lightweight to replace the heavy and bulky HF radio system,
- lightweight solar charger capable of charging all accessories as well as aircraft battery,
- Emergency Locator Transmitter (ELT) or Personal Locator Beacon (PLB) preferably linked to a GPS and capable of transmitting on the 406 mhz satellite frequency.

66

Survival kit – food and water:

- A minimum of 5lt/1gal of water per person in plastic 2 litre "Coke" bottles (preferably 10L/2.6gal especially in a dry hot climate). Plastic coke bottles are very strong and can be stowed under the seats and in the event of a crash you would not lose all your water.
- Carry enough high energy dry foods for 7 days per person, such as Soya and Maize meal or rice. These do not require a lot of water to prepare. Dried instant meal packs, used by hikers are also useful (just add hot water and eat).
- Survival biscuits, which are bland, but very high on energy.
- Soup, coffee and/or tea, sugar, salt, peanuts, dried fruit, multi-vitamins and chocolate bars.
- A small gas/solid fuel cooker and lightweight pot.
- Light weight plates, cups and cutlery.
- A roll of fishing line, wine bottle corks and some hooks as well as bait attachment thread.
- Bread, as it does not spoil quickly, is filling and can make an instant meal go a long way.
- Instant meals in cans, although heavy, they don't require any water or preparation and come in very handy when landing in a place where there is no food. Your food and water kit will often come in handy when having to overnight somewhere where there are no facilities, food or water available.

Survival kit – personal:

- a multi-tool,
- survival knife (one good quality folding pocket type with at least a 75mm / 3" blade plus another 150mm / 6" fixed blade for heavier duties),
- warm and practical clothing,

- good quality leather gloves,
- sewing kit with needle and strong thread suitable for repairing clothing, sleeping bag and tent etc.,
- life vest if flying over water/swamps,
- good thermal quality sleeping bag and tent,
- soap,
- toilet rolls,
- towel,
- mosquito repellent,
- solar shower bag (can be placed on top of the wing and will produce hot water after a few hours),
- lightweight collapsible vinyl bucket,
- lighter and waterproof matches,
- flint,
- small plastic magnifying glass (for starting fire as well as locating an insect sting or splinter),
- candles,
- 2 flashlights preferably LED types (one that can be worn on you head and another on your belt).

Survival kit – tools:

- axe suitable for use as a hammer for tie-down pegs as well as chopping wood etc.,
- small lightweight multi-purpose tree/hacksaw and or flexible saw,
- small lightweight spade,
- lightweight bush knife / machete.

Aircraft tools:

- set of wrenches (imperial sizes for American made aircraft),

- adjustable wrench,
- "Vice grip",
- spark plug wrench,
- small wire brush,
- multiple pliers,
- screwdrivers: one flat and one Phillips (your fuel tester may already have these attached),
- emergency tire inflation aerosol can,
- tire repair kit including a valve tool and small hand pump,
- 75-100mm / 3-4" length of rubber hose with a 50mm / 2" inside diameter and 3 hose clamps,
- 500mm / 2ft length of locking wire and a 1m / 3ft length of 1.5 mm / 1/16th" mild steel binding wire,
- 1 meter length of 0.5mm insulated electrical wire,
- roll of duct tape,
- piece of 600 grit sand paper,
- roll of electrical insulation tape,
- spare spark plug and magneto condenser (make sure that it is for the aircraft you are flying).

Fire extinguisher

Halon, Carbon Dioxide (CO_2) or BCF (Bromo-chloro-difluoro-methane) only. Never carry a dry powder type extinguisher for in-flight use as it can cause suffocation. In addition, it should always be mounted in a position that is easily accessible to the pilot.

First aid kit

Comprehensive up to date and specially packed for an aircraft that will be operating out in the remote bush with detailed first aid instructions and list of contents and their uses.

A small, cheap automotive, boat or household kit will not do. You will need some restricted medication such as severe pain killers, antibiotics and drips.

Consult a doctor, medic or pharmacist for assistance with this very important kit. It is recommended that you also have basic training in first aid.

Most pilots or aircraft owners buy a cheap first aid kit just to comply with the minimum regulations, place it in the back of the aircraft and forget about it. When they may need it in an emergency they discover that not only has everything expired and perished, but it does not contain the necessary items required to deal with the emergency.

The following list is a guide to the items that should be in a first aid kit in an aircraft that is operating out in remote, wild and inhospitable parts of the world:

- Analgesics (pain killers) for mild, moderate and very severe pain (i.e Morphine), pill and intravenous types. Know how, when and when not to administer the different types.
- Anti-inflammatory for muscular pain, swelling and inflammation.
- Antihistamine for allergies, insect bites and stings. Some types can also help against snake bites and adverse side effects from other medication.
- Antibiotics course suitable for most general types of infections.
- Rehydrating powders for relief from dehydration.
- Anti-diarrheal for relief of diarrhoea.
- Anti-malaria tablets.
- Malaria test kit.
- Medication for the relief of constipation.
- Medication for nausea and travel sickness.

- Medication for relief of gastro intestinal spasm and pain.
- Eye and ear drops.
- Water sterilization tablets or powder.
- Potassium permanganate. Can be used to sterilize water and as an antiseptic. It can also be used to start fires when mixed with a small amount of sugar (9:1).
- Savlon general purpose antiseptic liquid.
- Fryers balsam, helps stop bleeding.
- Antiseptic cream suitable for all insect bites, stings, cuts, abrasions and minor infections.
- Alcohol swabs.
- Antiseptic swabs.
- Plasters, assorted.
- Bandages, assorted.
- Surgical needle and thread. For stitching wounds.
- Butterfly strips for use in holding wounds together in place of needle and thread.
- Aerosol plastic spray on skin.
- Emergency foil blankets.
- Burn dressings/bandages, assorted sizes.
- Lip balm with sunscreen.
- Thermometer.
- Syringes and needles.
- Saline drip, tubing and needles. Know when, why and how to administer it properly.
- Tweezers.
- Hemostat. Valuable for stitching and clamping a severed blood vessel.
- Scissors.
- Safety pins – assorted.

- Surgical gloves.
- Cotton wool.
- Splints.
- Tourniquet.
- Suction bulb/syringe. For sucking poison from sting or bite.
- Antiseptic soap for scrubbing your hands.

Signaling equipment:
- signaling strips and instructions,
- mirror,
- rocket and ground flares.

Miscellaneous items:
- a plastic milk bottle crate (i.e. to be used to loose items in such as 2L Coke bottles or to make a trap),
- absorbent urinal bags,
- sick bags,
- fuel dipstick,
- fuel tester,
- engine oil,
- spare cowl, inspection cover screws and some nuts and bolts,
- Heavy duty (spring steel) tie-down pegs and strong marine rope (army tent pegs are excellent),
- Lightweight fuel cans, a large funnel and a length of clear siphon hose,
- Small hanging scale. Can be attached to the tie-down ring under the wing to weigh equipment and baggage,
- Couple of large garbage disposal bags,

Survival pouch (optional)

In addition to all the above a small compact survival pouch and water bottle attached to you or in a place where you can grab it quickly may be your only survival kit in the event of a fire when you're not able to salvage some of the above mentioned items.

The survival pouch should contain the following items:

- aluminum mess tin,
- miniature solid fuel burner,
- waterproof lighter,
- dehydrated high calorie food pack,
- emergency blanket,
- salt tablets,

Part 2. Survival techniques & procedures

The following section is based on the probability that most of the survival kit and equipment as mentioned in the previous section "Tools and Survival Equipment" is carried on board the aircraft. Furthermore that you, the pilot, is not incapacitated. When operating out in remote parts it is a good idea to thoroughly brief your passengers in case of such an incident so that they are familiar with all the tools and survival equipment on board the aircraft (as well as parts of this book).

Basics of survival

The four basic survival principles are (in order of importance):

1. Protection
2. Location
3. Water
4. Food

Prior to a forced landing

In the event of a forced landing and if time and circumstances allow, activate your Emergency Locator Transmitter (ELT) or Personal Locator Beacon (PLB), squawk 7700 on the transponder and call a may-day on the most appropriate frequency for the area and altitude you are. If your radio call is answered then if possible, check and supply your GPS coordinates or at least the approximate position.

After a forced landing

After a forced landing incident turn master switch and fuel selector off. Remove the first aid kit and fire extinguisher. Evacuate and ensure that crew and passengers are okay and deal with any first aid if required. Remove all survival equipment, water, food, tools and baggage as quickly as possible, as you will need as much of this as you can salvage to survive. If fuel is leaking from the aircraft, wait for engine to cool down sufficiently and then drain fuel. You will need fuel to start fires quickly and easily. Check the condition of the aircraft battery and disconnect and position it in an upright position, if required. You may need the battery to power radios or signalling light etc.

Camp site and shelter

Set up camp as soon as possible and collect fire wood. The four most important things you need to concentrate on immediately are: Shelter, Fire, Food and Water. Choose dry, high ground. If the aircraft is in a suitable location and not too badly damaged, then it can also be used as part of the camp site for shelter and storing valuable items etc. Remember that although the aircraft may be damaged, you may still need to securely tie it down as the wings will still produce lift and the airplane may be blown over during severe windy conditions. If necessary, secure long thin logs and or branches on top of the wings to act as spoilers that will break down any lift created over the wings by high winds.

If you have a tent, pitch it under the wing as this will usually offer better protection from the elements. If you are carrying a large lightweight tarpaulin, place it over the wing to form an "A"-frame. This will increase the size of the shelter and offer even more warmth and protection.

If you do not have a tent or a tarpaulin, the airplane may have to serve as the shelter. In addition an "A"-frame shelter can easily be erected and joined to the wings out of trees, using your survival tools and hardware such as an axe, saw, rope, wire etc. The aircraft upholstery can be used to waterproof the shelter.

Latrine

Prepare a latrine far enough away from the camp site or a river to prevent spreading bacteria and contamination. Select an area that is as much as possible downwind from the camp site. Camp hygiene is of paramount importance! Always wash your hands especially before handling food. Regardless to whether or not water is scarce, at least place a covered container next to the latrine filled with water and mixed with a strong antiseptic solution such as potassium permanganate or Savlon.

Dig a round or square hole about 300mm wide as deep as possible in the ground and leave the soil in a heap within reach. Every time you use the latrine immediately cover the deposits with just enough sand to prevent smell and the attraction of flies. Once full, cover completely and dig another hole.

For a more long term camp you can make the hole wider and deeper and build up around the sides of the hole with rocks and mud to form walls and then place logs across the top to form a seat leaving only a sufficient hole for use. The gaps in the logs should also be sealed with wet ash from the camp fire.

Establishing communication

If the aircraft is equipped with an Emergency Locator Transmitter (ELT) and or you have a Personal Locator Beacon (PLB), make sure that they are transmitting. If the aircraft ELT antenna appears damaged, either repair the antenna or remove the ELT unit from the fuselage and attach the portable antenna that should be attached to the case. Ensure that the antenna has an unobstructed area around it and that it is erected vertically.

Capture and store the GPS coordinates of your position. Attempt radio, cellular or satellite telephone communication. In the event of the aircraft VHF antennas being damaged and you don't have a handheld radio or satellite telephone, cut off the coaxial cable at the base of the antenna, pull the end outside the aircraft and fabricate an antenna with a 600mm/2ft length of electrical wire attached to the centre wire at the end of the coaxial cable. This is the correct ¼ wave antenna length for VHF aviation frequencies. If you have a solar charger panel, use it to charge the battery during the day. If you have an HF Radio, check and if necessary, repair the 'long wire' antenna.

Signalling

Prepare signalling devises for use when required. Set out ground to air signalling strips or carve out the signals into soft sand. Set up a separate special signalling fireplace away from camp and place a fuel can and lighter/matches next to the fireplace. Collect lots of green branches/grass and engine oil to generate smoke. Remember that upholstery and tyres give off black smoke when burned and this may be more beneficial for search and rescue, as normal bush and veld fires create white smoke.

Once you can clearly see an aircraft approaching in your direction, start the signal fire and use plenty fresh branches, grass and engine oil to generate lots of smoke. You can also use the mirror from the signal strip kit to try attracting attention. Once the aircraft is close by and heading towards you, shoot off an aerial flare and when it appears to be banking or circling in your direction then ignite a ground flare.

Remove an aircraft landing light and extend the wires to be able to signal to an over flying aircraft at night. Aim the beam of light directly at the aircraft and using a sweeping action, flash the Morse code "SOS" (... _ _ _ ...) in the same manner as using a mirror.

Three fast sweeps, three slow sweeps and again three fast sweeps. Aircraft strobe lights can also be used to attract attention.

Ground to air signal codes

This code is designed for use by survivors, the symbols shown below are laid out flat on the ground using pieces of fabric, stones or any other means at your disposal. The symbols should be at least 3 metres (10 feet) in height or larger if possible. Care should be taken to lay out the symbols exactly as depicted in the drawings, to avoid any confusion with other symbols. A space of 3 metres (10 feet) should separate the layout 2, 7, 10, 14 and 17. An effort should be made to provide as big a color contrast as possible between the materials used and the background against witch it is laid. In addition to laying out these symbols, every effort is to be made to attract attention by means of radio, flares, smoke or other available means. When smoke or fire is used as a means of attracting attention, locate three evenly spaced fires across wind.

No.	Message	Code Symbol
1.	Require doctor - serious injuries	I
2.	Require medical supplies	I I
3.	Unable to proceed	X
4.	Require food and water	F
5.	Require firearms and ammunition	⋁
6.	Require map and compass	☐
7.	Require signal lamp with battery & radio	⁚
8.	Indicate direction to proceed	K
9.	Am proceeding in this direction	↑
10.	Will attempt to take-off	I⟩
11.	Aircraft seriously damaged	⌐
12.	Probably safe to land here	△
13.	Require fuel and oil	L
14.	All well	L L
15.	No	N
16.	Yes	Y
17.	Not understood	⌐L
18.	Require mechanic	W

Food and water

Don't rely solely on your emergency food and water supply. You will need to find other food and water as it's only a matter of time before your rations will run out, especially water. Ration out the food and water in your survival kit. It is also important to keep in mind that eating increases the demand for water intake.

Plants

Many plants and roots are edible. Discard any plant that has a creamy or milky sap as it's probably poisonous (an exception is the dandelion).

Rub a small portion of the juices or sap on the inside of your bottom lip. Also place a small piece of the plant on the tip of your tongue. You can also put some of the juices under your arm pit. Wait about 5 minutes. If you detect any stinging, burning or putrid sensation then discard the plant. If you don't detect any of these symptoms then take a larger piece of the plant, chew it and swallow it. Wait two hours. If you experience any stomach upset or nausea discard the plant as its probably poisonous. If you don't detect any of these symptoms then take an even larger piece, chew and swallow and wait a further two hours. If you feel no ill effects then the plant is probably safe to eat. Boil the plant, discard the juices and eat only the plant.

Worms, insects & snakes

Worms and insects are high on nutrition. Termites, locusts, ants, bees and wasps etc. are all edible, some quite tasty and are found in most parts. They are easy to prepare by frying or boiling or can be eaten raw.

Brightly coloured insects, caterpillars, frogs and snails should be avoided as they may be poisonous.

Snakes are edible, similar to fish. Cut off its head well behind the poison sacks, similar to gutting a fish, slice open the belly all the way to the tail with your knife blade pointing outwards, so not to pierce the innards. Gut, clean, chop into steaks or fillets and place on fire or fry.

Trapping

Trapping small animals and birds is not that difficult. Use your plastic milk crate or a box and fishing gut to make a trap to catch small animals and birds. If you do not have a crate or box, you can fabricate a cage out of branches and wire. An aircraft cargo net can also be used for trapping. Catch fish with the fishing line, hooks and bottle corks, using bugs ad worms as bait. You can easily make a simple snare from rope, wire or even fishing gut. The aircraft ADF or HF long wire antenna can be used for this purpose too. Tie the one end of the snare to a secure shrub or tree, tie a noose and set only large enough to catch an animal's leg or neck and suspend the noose on top of brush about 100mm/4" above the ground and camouflage well. Another example is the spring snare, this as a noose attached to a bent over a tree that is secured to a hook in a stump or log. When an animal enters the noose and disturbs it, the hook is dislodged and the animal is drawn up and suspended in the air. Laying bait under a trap will attract animals to it. *(Refer to Figures 10 and 11)*.

There are various ways of making snares and other kinds of traps, however, it is beyond the scope of this book.

A firearm, crossbow or bow is a major advantage for killing animals to eat as well as protection. Its illegal to carry firearms across most borders of the world, however, a crossbow or bow may not be restricted and will make a very valuable part of your survival kit.

Figure 9. Box trap.

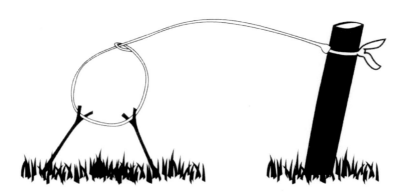

Figure 10. Simple snare.

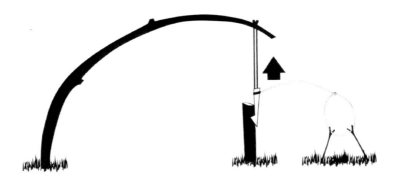

Figure 11. Spring snare.

Preparing the kill

Bleeding - Hang the animal by its hind legs from a tree or suitable structure. Cut its throat from ear to ear making sure that you cut through the jugular vein. Leave to bleed until no more blood drips. If a bird, cut the head off.

Skinning – With the knife blade outwards cut around the legs and down the centre of the belly taking care not to cut into the stomach or digestive organs. Pull the skin off slowly, starting at the back legs. Birds are normally not skinned only plucked.

Gutting – Cut into the breast as low as possible, taking care not to cut into the internal organs. Cut all the way up to the anus. Cut through the membrane and remove the heart, lungs and wind pipe. After all the guts have fallen out, carefully inspect the carcass to make sure you haven't missed anything and also make sure that the anus is clear. If a bird, make an insertion between the tail and vent and draw all the innards out by hand.

If you have water to spare, rinse off the carcass.

Fire and cooking

Besides the camp fire or a portable gas cooker in your survival kit, you can also make a small cooker by putting fuel and sand into a tin can and lighting it, it will burn a long time. This device can also be used as a fire lighter to start a camp fire, if the wood is slightly damp. Try not to use the emergency gas/solid fuel cooker as you may need it to cook indoors during bad weather.

Finding water

If you find a river or stream, your water problem will be sorted out. However, if there are no rivers or streams, you will still need to find or make a water supply. Look for water in low lying areas as water always drains downhill. If there are animal tracks, you could follow them to possible water. Digging into dry river beds at the low point of a bend may also reveal water. Lush green vegetation in an otherwise dry area may be a sign of water.

You can also collect water from rain and condensation by using plastic sheeting. Tying a plastic bag around a lush green branch will produce water from condensation *(see figure 12)*. A fair amount of water can be collected by a solar still. Construct a solar still by digging a 1m/3ft wide and 50cm/2ft deep hole in the ground. Place a container in the centre of the hole. Cover the hole with a piece of plastic sheet or bag, allowing it to sag down into the hole forming a funnel. Place a small stone in the centre to help keep its funnel shape. Water condenses underneath the plastic sheet, runs down and drips into the container. Rain water and overnight condensation can also be collected in the top of the funnel. Make sure that you place enough rocks or dig enough sand around the sides to prevent it from collapsing into the hole. Lush moist branches, plants and cacti can be placed in the hole around the collection container to provide more moisture for condensation. If at the coast, then wide, shallow containers of salt water can be placed around the collection container too. (*Refer to Figure 13*).

Salt water, contaminated water and even urine can be distilled using an off the shelf distillation kit. The other option is to fabricate one from two containers of which the one must be of metal construction and a length of tubing. Fill up a tin can or something similar with the water and seal the top allowing only the tube to stick out. Place the container on a fire and run the tube into a suitably covered collection container. When the water boils, the steam will condensate in the tube and top of collection container and turn into purified and drinkable water. (*Refer to Figure 14*).

Figure 12. Tree branch still.

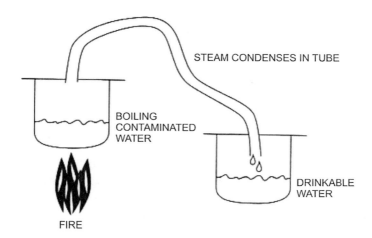

Figure 13.Solar still.

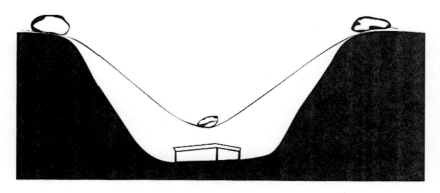

Figure 14. Ground still.

Walking to find help

To increase your chances of discovery it is always better to stay with the aircraft. However, if you really need to look for help, at least have a well thought out plan in place before leaving the camp and ensure that everyone agrees and understands all plans of action. If you are alone, leave clear signals as to which direction you are going. If it is necessary to walk to a nearby location on the map for help, first plot a line on your aviation chart as you would for air navigation. Place the map on a flat surface and place your pocket plotting compass or the aircraft compass on the line. Determine where North is and position the map to face north. Read off the magnetic heading to walk by observing the heading indicated on the compass rose down the line. Then look for landmarks on the horizon to walk to in that direction.

In addition, if you have a portable GPS, plot the co-ordinates of the destination on your map, enter them into the GPS and use it to navigate, but keep the chart and compass handy in the event of the batteries going flat.

Limit all walking during the midday heat. Attempt to start walking just prior to sunrise, resting in shade when too hot and continuing in the late afternoon until sunset. You will conserve a lot of water this way.

If both the handheld radio and the aircraft radio are operational, take the handheld to communicate with your camp at set times. Use the emergency frequency 121.5 or approach or centre frequency that you are under to communicate on. This will increase the chances of an airliner receiving your transmissions. Remember to conserve battery power.

Part 3. First aid

It is advisable for every pilot to attend a First Aid course. In an emergency it is very difficult to first have to read First Aid Instructions. It is better to be prepared.

Always carry a fully comprehensive up-to-date kit specially packed for aviation and survival out in remote areas. A cheap automotive or household kit is unacceptable and will not do. If you carry medicines and equipment that are prescription and restricted types make sure you know how to administer them properly.

The following information should be used as a guideline only.

Before administering first aid:

1. Check if the patient is breathing. If not, immediately start resuscitation procedures. See "Emergency Resuscitation Procedures" below.
2. Check for bleeding.
3. Check for other injuries.

Note: Do not move the patient unless there is danger of explosion or fire.

Bleeding

Blood loss can be dangerous, treat it immediately. Severe blood loss is life threatening.

1. Apply *constant*, direct pressure with a sterile bandage or clean cloth. If clean material is not available, use your bare hand.
2. Elevate the limb, unless you suspect a broken bone.
3. If bandages become blood soaked, place a clean bandage on top of the soiled one. **Do not** replace the soiled bandage because a

release in pressure will interfere with normal clotting and increase the chance of infection.

4. ***Do not*** try to cleanse a deep wound or apply medication. Use only Saline (Sodium Chloride 0,9%) solution to rinse wounds.
5. Keep the patient lying down. Severe bleeding will lead to shock.
6. Place a blanket under and on top of the patient to maintain body temperature.
7. ***Do not*** allow ingestion of any solids or fluids.

Note: Pressure points should be used only if bleeding will stop. Tourniquets can cause severe damage and should be used only as a last resort.

Broken bones

(Broken bones are not usually life-threatening).

1. ***Do not*** move the patient or injured limb.
2. Stop serious bleeding.
3. ***Do not*** straighten a limb.
4. ***Do not*** push a protruding bone into the skin. Apply a sterile bandage, but no ointment.
5. Keep the patient warm and lying down to prevent shock.
6. ***Do not*** allow ingestion of solids or fluids.

Neck, head or back injuries

Exercise extreme caution.

1. ***Do not*** move the patient unless there is extreme danger of explosion or fire.
2. ***Do not*** move the head or neck. Even small movement could cause further injury and paralysis.
3. ***Do not*** allow ingestion of any solids or fluids, not even water.

Note: Head injuries may cause drowsiness, nausea, unequal pupils and combative behaviour.

Drowning

Do not attempt to drain water from the lungs. Patients usually die from lack of air, not from water in the lungs or stomach.

1. Place the patient on his back and start resuscitation procedures.
2. Keep the patient warm and lying down.

Burns

Minor thermal burns (the burned area is red, usually no blisters).

1. Immerse in cool water. Do not use ice or ice water.
2. *Do not* use ointments. Use a Saline solution to rinse.
3. Cover with a special burn dressing or sterile bandage.

Major thermal burns (the burned areas is greater than 10% - as a guide the palm of a person's hand equals 1% of the body area of the body - usually blisters; skin may be torn away or broken)

1. Wrap the patient in a clean, dry sheet or smooth, textured material.
2. *Do not* use blankets or rough, textured materials as lint and fibers could contaminate the burn.
3. *Do not* use ointments etc.
4. *Do not* remove anything sticking to the skin.
5. *Do not* open blisters.
6. *Do not* ingest any solids or liquids.

Emergency resuscitation procedures

When heartbeat and breathing stop, a person will be clinically or biologically dead within about 5 minutes, unless emergency resuscitation procedures are started. Keep in mind that proper resuscitation efforts can keep patients alive indefinitely, but attempts to restore breathing without also restoring the heartbeat will not be successful.

Open air passage

If the patient is unconscious and not breathing, lay him on his back and open his air passage.

1. Clear mouth of mucus and foreign objects.
2. Raise neck with one hand, tilt head as far back as possible to keep patient's tongue from blocking airway.

Note: **Do not** *tilt the head of an infant back. The neck is very pliable and tilting the head backward may block the passage instead of opening it.*

Artificial breathing

If the patient is still not breathing, begin artificial breathing for him.

1. Close the patient's nostrils with fingers, and keep patient's head tilted backwards.
2. Make a tight seal by placing your mouth completely over the patient's mouth. Cover both mouth and nose of an infant.
3. Exhale into patient's mouth and watch chest expand. Give two slow, full breaths. For an infant, do not blow vigorously. Use small puffs of air.
4. Watch patient's chest fall while listening for air return between breaths.
5. If the airway is blocked, try back blows, abdominal or chest thrusts, and/or finger probes until airway is open.

Note: Breathe for adults once every five seconds; for children once every four seconds, for infants once every three seconds.

Pulse

Adults and Children

Feel for carotid pulse on either side of patient's Adam's apple.

Infants

Check for pulse located on the inside of the upper arm, midway between the elbow and the shoulder.

Artificial circulation

If pulse is absent, begin artificial circulation. Continue without interruption until advanced life support equipment is available.

For adults:

1. Place heel of hand over lower half of breastbone and cover with other hand.
2. Press down firmly and quickly 1.5 to 2 inches and release.
3. In case of only one rescuer, use 15 external heart compressions at the rate of 80 to 100 per minute, followed by two slow, full breaths. Then repeat 15 compressions.
4. In case of two rescuers, one performs 3 external heart massages and the other one breathing – give five external heart compressions at the rate of 90 to 100 per minute, and inflate the patient's lungs after every fifth compression.

For Children:

1. Place heel of hand over lower half of breastbone. Use the heel of only one hand for compressions.
2. Press down firmly and quickly 1 to 1.5 inches and release.
3. Use five external heart compressions at the rate of 80 to 100 per minute, and inflate the child's lungs after every fifth compression.

For Infants:

1. Draw an imaginary line between the nipples to locate the breastbone.

2. Place the index finger of the hand furthest from the infant's head under the imaginary line where it intersects with the breastbone. The compression is one finger's width below this intersection, at the location of the middle and ring fingers.

3. Press down firmly and quickly 0.5 to 1 inch and release.

4. Use five external heart compressions at the rate of 100 per minute, and inflate the infant's lungs after every fifth compression.

CHAPTER 6

CAMPING

Backcountry camping

47.

Landing on a backcountry trail to camp.

48.

Camping

This section is primarily about recreational or expedition camping. However, some of the information here is also applicable to an emergency survival camp site, provided the equipment listed is carried on board the aircraft. For setting up a camp site under emergency conditions refer to the section on "Survival".

What to take with

If you are going far out into the wild and remote bush or mountains, I'd consider virtually everything in the "Tools and Survival" checklist *(refer to chapter on "Tools & Survival Equipment")*.

The following checklist is additional to the survival checklist:

- Sufficient fuel to get there and back. Not too much as you may need to leave some behind in case of a hot & high short field take-off.
- Lots of water. Remember you can easily land in a short space heavy, then dump all excess water to take-off again. I normally take enough excess water in my empty fuel cans for washing and showering etc. It is a bonus if you have a river nearby.
- Small 1m x 1m / 3ft x 3ft piece of plastic tarpaulin sheet.
- Plastic basin for washing, cooking utensils and clothing.
- Soap for personal use as well as washing clothes and cooking utensils etc.
- Toilet paper (more than you normally carry in your survival equipment).
- Firearm or crossbow/bow.
- Food as required.
- Lightweight lantern.
- Extra rope.

This may seem like a lot of weight. If you exclude the excess water and consumables such as food and drink and you're only two persons in a 4-place airplane without the rear seats, you are in fact only carrying the same weight as a third adult for the take-off. If you're alone then you're only carrying the same weight as two people.

SETTING UP CAMP

Securing the airplane

After landing the first thing you need to do is to secure the aircraft properly in case of a sudden weather change, especially if landing out in the mountains.

Use the rear of your axe and hammer in all the tie down pegs in the best position (45°) away from wing tie down rings. Don't forget to tie down the tail section too. You can never have enough rope.

Find a level area on dry high ground to tie the plane down, using the most secure method possible (refer to the chapter on tying down an aircraft). Sometimes it's difficult to decide were the prevailing winds are, especially if you've landed in a mountain area for the first time. Winds often change 180° around noon.

Place rocks against the wheels, especially if the airplane is on a down slope.

If it's the rainy season, collect two long and straight branches or a small tree, trim off excess branches and place them on the ground near the airplane. You may need these to tie them on top of the wings to act as spoilers in case of an approaching thunderstorm.

Ensure that all electrical switches are off, so that you don't accidentally drain the battery during starting.

If the airplane is not standing on level ground, turn the fuel selector off or onto one tank only to prevent cross feed. Place a sun shield on the inside of the windshield.

Tent

Now that the airplane is secure, the next thing is your tent. The best place for this is directly under the one wing with the door of the tent facing the plane, as you will have better protection in case of wind and rain. Don't forget to securely tie and peg the tent down.

It is better to pitch your tent under the right wing as the right seat doesn't require complicated rail stops. It may go further forward than the left seat allowing easier and wider access into the rear of the plane to get to supplies and equipment.

In addition to this you can quickly and easily remove the seat to use as a seat outside. The right side door should have quick release hinge pins (these are fairly easy to fit), so that you can easily and quickly remove the door out of the way if required.

Tarpaulin "A"-frame

If you are carrying a large lightweight tarpaulin, then place it over the wing to form an "A"-frame shelter and allow a reasonable opening near the fuselage facing the rear of plane. Tie/peg it down.

Now you will have a comfortable living area with double protection from the elements. Under the "A"-frame you will have your tent on far end towards the wing tip, allowing for additional space between the tent and fuselage, you still have the inside of the plane, too. You may also be able to remove the right side door.

Place your sleeping bags and mattresses as well as any other personal belongings you may need during the night in the tent, as well as a candle and matches, lighter or other light source. Keep clothing and valuables in the tent.

Latrine

Use your spade to prepare a latrine far enough away from a river to prevent contamination of the water and from the camp site and flies from bothering you and spreading bacteria. Select an area that is as much as possible downwind from the camp site.

Dig a round or square hole about 200-300mm wide as deep as possible and leave the soil in a heap within reach. Every time you use the latrine immediately cover the deposits and toilet paper with just enough sand to prevent smell and the attraction of flies. Once full, cover completely and dig another hole.

For a more long term camp you can make the hole wider and deeper and build up around the sides of the hole with rocks and mud to form walls and then place logs across the top to form a seat leaving only a sufficient hole for use. The gaps in the logs should also be sealed with wet ash from the camp fire.

Fire place

Choose and prepare a safe spot for this, so that even in very windy conditions there is no risk of a grass fire or hot embers blowing onto tent or plane. Using a spade make a shallow hollow in the ground and clear sufficient grass from the ground all around the pit. Place a pile of sand and some very leafy branches on the ground nearby to use as fire beaters. Remember that you also have the airplane's fire extinguisher.

Kitchen table

The airplane's horizontal stabilizer makes an excellent work table. It can be used for preparing food or as a table for your laptop etc.

Communication

In case of an emergency you may need to communicate with the outside world. If you have a sat phone, set it up and test it.

Check for cell phone reception.

Use your hand held radio for a radio check on the local traffic advisory frequency or listen for an aircraft broadcasting nearby and call it for a radio check. Also try calling other aircraft on a local area control frequency and also the emergency frequency 121.5.

Turn off all devices to conserve battery power, unless you have a solar charger.

Remember that the aircraft radio is more powerful than the handheld radio, so if you get no response from another aircraft, try using the aircraft radio to transmit. But be careful as this could drain the battery making it difficult to start the engine.

Showers

Fill up your solar showers and place them on top of the wing opposite to the tent. By the afternoon you should have hot water to wash with. Find a rock and place on the ground nearby to place your soap on or you can place the soap on top of the wing, too, but it's difficult to find the soap on top of the wing whilst taking a shower. If it's a very sandy area under the wing and you don't have a small ground tarpaulin, use a large garbage disposal bag, if you forgot that, then make a plan so you don't have mud everywhere. And dig a trench so that the waste water can drain away.

Conserve water by only using sufficient to apply soap, then again to rinse off. Solar camp showers normally hold about 15ltr of water and you can get 4 showers out of them. I normally carry two of them, because they are so light.

Scullery area

Find a suitable place for this away from your camp site and dig a hole in the ground. After washing up discard the waste water into the hole and lightly cover over so as to prevent attracting flies, animals and ants. All scraps must be burned in the camp fire.

Washing line

If your airplane has an ADF or HF long wire antenna, this makes a perfect washing line. So even if you have removed your old ADF or HF radio, keep the antenna wire on the airplane.

Otherwise, you can take just a piece of rope, tie it between two trees; you can also make use even of the tie-down ropes which are already attached to the plane. Of course, it helps to take some pegs with, too.

Rivers

Never pollute a river by discarding any waste into it. Only collect water from the river for use in the camp site and properly discard all waste water in a suitable pit away from the river. Water from a river should always be treated, distilled or boiled prior to consumption.

Weather

Pay attention to the daily weather. Monitor the winds and the build up of clouds day and night, so that you may know what to expect during your planned departure.

Winds in the mountains can change direction by 180° between early morning and afternoon.

Once the camp site is set-up, you should be able to live quite comfortably.

Author landing on the shore of a lake and camping

49. Short final approach.

50. Short field landing.

51. Camp.

BREAKING CAMP

Garbage disposal

Cover up all holes and pits such as the latrine and washing area properly. Do not leave ANY garbage lying around. All garbage such as plastic and tin cans should be burned, crushed and buried to help with organic decomposition.

Dumping excess water

Dump excess water as necessary for a safe take-off, particularly any remaining water in fuel cans as you cannot drink it.

If you intend to return again soon you could hide a few coke bottles filled with water under dense shrubs or you bury them under the ground. Cover them so that animals, especially monkeys and baboons, will not find them. That way you'll have more water available for the next time you return. Excess fuel can also be stored in the same manner.

Environmentally conscious

It is good practice to ensure that you leave the site as it was prior to your arrival. Do not litter!

Loading the airplane

Remember, if taking off in a soft or rough area, load the aircraft properly, so as to keep the nose light during the take-off roll.

Pre-flight

Carefully examine the airplane, take-off area/airstrip, temperatures, elevation, density altitude and winds prior to your departure.

CHAPTER 7

AIRCRAFT TECHNICAL

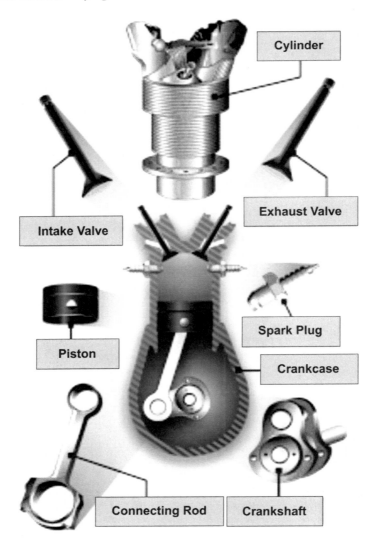

Figure 15. The 4-stroke internal combustion aircraft engine.

Aircraft Technical

Part 1. Reciprocating / 4-stroke internal combustion aircraft engine

The reciprocating engine is also known as an internal-combustion engine. This name is used because the fuel mixture is burned within the engine. To understand how a reciprocating engine works, we must first study the parts and the functions they perform.

The seven major parts are:
- cylinders,
- pistons,
- connecting rods,
- crankshaft,
- valves,
- spark plugs,
- camshaft (not shown).

Refer to the relative location of these parts in figure 15.

Engine operation

The cylinder is closed on one end (the cylinder head) and the piston fits snuggly in the cylinder. The piston wall is grooved to accommodate rings, which fit tightly against the cylinder wall to help seal the cylinder's open end, so that gases cannot escape from the combustion chamber. The combustion chamber is the area between the top of the piston and the head of the cylinder when the piston is at its uppermost point of travel.

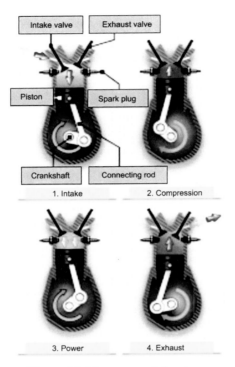

Figure 16. Movement of the piston.

The up-and-down movement of the piston is converted to rotary motion to turn the propeller by the connecting rod and the crankshaft, just as in most automobiles.

Note the crankshaft, connecting rod and piston arrangement and imagine how the movement of the piston is converted to the rotary motion of the crankshaft. Note particularly how the connecting rod is joined to the crankshaft in an offset manner.

The valves at the top of the cylinder open and close to let in a mixture of fuel and air and to let out (exhaust) burnt gases from the combustion chamber. The opening and closing of the valves is done by a camshaft which is geared to the crankshaft. This gearing arrangement ensures that the two valves open and close at the proper times.

Now let's consider the movement of the piston (four strokes) and the five events of a cycle *(see figure 16)*.

1. The intake stroke

The cycle begins with the piston at top centre. As the crankshaft pulls the piston downward, a partial vacuum is created in the cylinder chamber. The cam arrangement has opened the intake valve, and the vacuum causes a mixture of fuel and air to be drawn into the cylinder.

2. Compression and ignition stroke

As the crankshaft drives the piston upward in the cylinder, the fuel and air mixture is compressed. The intake valve has closed, of course, as this upward stroke begins. As the compression stroke is completed, just before the piston reaches its top position, the compressed mixture is ignited by the spark plug.

3. Power stroke

The very hot gases expand with tremendous force, not an explosion, driving the piston down and turning the crankshaft. The valves are also closed during this stroke.

4. Exhaust stroke

On the second upward stroke (or outward, according to the direction the unit is pointed), the exhaust valve is opened and the burned gases are forced out by the piston.

At the moment the piston completes the exhaust stroke, the cycle is started again by the intake stroke. Each piston within the engine must make four strokes to complete one cycle, and this complete cycle occurs hundreds of times per minute as the engine runs.

The overall principles of reciprocating-engine operation are easy to understand if you remember what happens with each stroke that the piston makes.

ENGINE MANAGEMENT

Pre-flight cylinder lubrication and compression test

As part of your first pre-flight of the day, especially in cold weather, it may be a good idea to pull the propeller through all compression strokes (i.e. four times for a four cylinder engine and six times for a six cylinder engine etc.) to check for any low compression and at the same time pre-lubricate the cylinder walls as well as many other parts of the engine.

This procedure will add longevity to the engine and save thousands on cylinder repairs and top overall, the same time it will give you an early warning to pending cylinder problems such as combustion chamber cracks, leaking valves and broken or worn rings.

Warning: Prior to touching the propeller, ensure that the magnetos are both off, the mixture is at idle cut-off, the throttle is fully closed and the wheels are chocked. It is for this reason that you should always do a "dead cut" check on the magnetos at idle prior to shutting down the engine.

Pre-start priming

Pre-start priming is necessary in order to prevent excessive wear and tear to both, the starter motor and the battery. Prime the engine as per normal, then with the mags off, mixture cut off and throttle closed, carefully pull the propeller through two compressions.

When you get into the airplane and push the starter button, the engine should fire up almost instantly.

Throttle and pitch control

The first sign of an inexperienced pilot is very harsh and abrupt changes of throttle and propeller pitch settings as well as all other controls during the various phases of flight, especially noticeable during the approach to land *(see "Stabilized approach" under the Bush Flying section)*.

The sign of a professional is a gentle, smooth adjustment of the throttle and propeller controls, as well as all other controls.

Mixture control (EGT)

Correct mixture control is critical, if you want to get a long life out of your engine. If your aircraft has got an EGT gauge that is only connected to one cylinder, then it is always safer to run it richer than normal, as you do not know how lean the other cylinders are burning.

For example, if your EGT gauge is connected to cylinder number 1 and you lean it to just under peak, you may be at risk of over leaning one of the other cylinders. Eventually, this may result in major damage to that cylinder and even possible engine failure during flight.

Most pilots make the mistake of leaning the "hottest" cylinder.

If your aircraft is equipped with an EGT gauge connected to all cylinders or an engine analyser, then the following procedure should be used to determine peak EGT settings for your engine:

1. Climb to 6000ft at full power, preferably with mixture full rich or as rich as possible.
2. Level off at 65% power.
3. Select cylinder 1 on the engine analyser / EGT gauge.
4. Lean mixture control until the EGT stops climbing and starts to drop.

5. Note the highest temperature and if possible the fuel flow at which cylinder number 1 EGT stopped climbing and started to descend. This cylinder has now reached peak EGT.

6. Go to full rich mixture.

7. Select cylinder number 2.

8. Wait for a stabilized EGT on cylinder 2.

9. Repeat steps 3 to 6 above on the remaining cylinders.

You have now established the peak EGT on all cylinders.

Now select the cylinder that had the lowest peak EGT. This is your critical cylinder. For cruise power settings up to 75% power, the EGT should be 75-100° cool of this cylinders EGT. For higher power settings the EGT should be about 150-200° rich (cooler) of peak established for the critical cylinder.

All other cylinders will be richer and so will be well within a safe operating EGT.

By adhering to the above mentioned advice, your cylinders and engine will last longer.

Determining the leanest cylinder without EGT gauge

If you want to install a single-cylinder EGT probe into the leanest cylinder, you need to know which is the leanest cylinder for the average conditions that you fly. Fly the aircraft and establish your cruise power settings and altitude. Lean the aircraft normally. Land the airplane and remove the top spark plugs. The spark plug with the lightest colour deposits should be the leanest cylinder. The best time to do this test is just after you have installed new spark plugs or cleaned the old ones.

Cylinder head temperatures (CHT)

After starting the engine, allow it to warm up to a minimum operating CHT before taxiing or doing power checks.

Never close the power and put the nose down to lose altitude quickly. This will almost definitely result in a cracked cylinder head, sooner rather than later. This is known as "shock cooling". When descending gradually come off the power, but try at all times to keep the power on as much as possible during a descent or approach to land. MAP and RPM should remain in the green at all times. Many skydiving aircraft suffer with cracked cylinders in the hands of inexperienced pilots.

After landing don't forget to open the cowl flaps and allow the engine to idle for a few minutes, so the CHTs can stabilize prior to shutting down. This is even more critical for turbo charged engines.

MAINTENANCE AND REPAIRS

The following mechanical and electrical problems are quite common and when they occur, you may not be at the holding point on a busy airfield with a maintenance facility to taxi back to. You may well be hundreds of miles out in the remote bush. A bush pilot has to be able to fix minor mechanical, airframe and electrical problems on an aircraft.

ENGINE MALFUNCTIONS, DIAGNOSTICS AND REPAIRS

Magneto drop

If you experience a severe drop in engine RPM on one magneto during your pre-take-off engine checks, it is more than likely a fouled spark plug caused by excessive idling with a rich mixture. This common problem can be prevented by immediately leaning the mixture shortly after starting the engine and during the taxi.

To clear the problem, set the engine RPM at 2000 or higher, lean out the mixture and run the engine, frequently checking the magnetos until the RPM is back up to normal.

If this does not solve the problem you will have to shut down and remove the cowling. Identify the "faulty magneto" (i.e. if sitting in aircraft the left mag will be on the left hand side of the engine and right mag on the right hand side).

Magnetos are easy to identify as they are two black devices attached to the rear or top of the engine with either 4 or 6 thick high tension spark plug wires coming out of the rear of each one. A four cylinder engine will have four HT cables per magneto and a six cylinder engine six cables.

Once you have identified the faulty mag, trace the HT wires to spark plugs from the mag and remove the spark plugs. Normally one mag will power the top spark plugs on the one side of the engine and the bottom spark plugs on the opposite side of the engine.

DO NOT DROP SPARK PLUGS! (Be careful not to damage the ceramic insulation around the anode or terminal.) Carefully inspect, clean and replace, if required. Also carefully inspect all HT cables and connectors for damage.

If this has not solved the problem, then you may have to fly the aircraft with mag drop to the nearest place with a maintenance shop. It is acceptable to fly the aircraft with this problem, as an aircraft engine is equipped with two magnetos and two spark plugs per cylinder. As long as the other magneto and spark plug is operational, all the cylinders will be firing.

Often after take-off the problem clears itself. However, it is still a good idea to check it after landing, as you may have an intermittent or cracked spark plug.

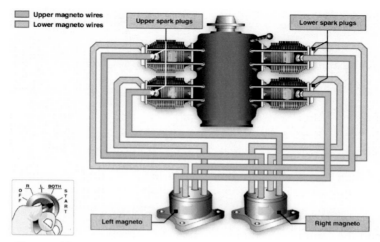

Figure 17. Four cylinder engine showing the position of the magnetos & high tension spark plug cables.

Dead magneto - engine dies completely when one of the magnetos is selected

Remove the cowling. Identify the faulty mag (i.e. if sitting in aircraft the left mag will be on the left hand side of the engine and right mag on the right hand side). Locate a thin wire attached to the mag and either disconnect or cut it. Start the engine and conduct a standard mag check.

If the problem has been solved, more than likely the wire is either shorting to ground somewhere or the magneto/ignition switch is faulty. Leave the wire off and fly the aircraft. However, be aware that this mag will now be "live" after shut down.

If this does not solve the problem, it is possible that the condenser, points or coil inside the magneto may be faulty and this will have to be repaired by a qualified or competent person with specialized equipment.

You may need to fly the aircraft on one mag to the nearest place with a maintenance shop. If the repair shop doesn't have a replacement condenser, take the spare one from your tool kit and have the mechanic fit it to the faulty mag.

Rough running engine after start up

If the engine runs rough similar to a magneto drop but both magnetos appear operational with no unusual RPM drop, more than likely one cylinder is low on compression or has excessive blow-by past the rings, valve seat or a cylinder is cracked somewhere (possibly due to shock cooling) or in rare cases, both spark plugs may be fouled in one of the cylinders (possibly due to a broken piston oil ring).

Remove the cowling. Remove the oil filler cap. Ensure that both magnetos are off and the fuel selector valve is shut off. It's a good idea to also disconnect all the spark plug leads from the spark plugs for safety. This will ensure that the engine will definitely not be able to start.

Slowly turn the propeller around whilst listening for any loud hissing sounds coming from the engine. If a hissing sound comes from outside of the cylinders, you may have a crack in a cylinder head or combustion chamber.

If sounds come out of the oil filler neck, dipstick or crankcase breather tube, you can suspect at least one broken piston compression ring or aligned ring gaps.

If sounds come out of the carburettor air intake (Air filter), an intake valve may not be seating correctly or there is a crack about the valve seat.

If sounds come out of the exhaust pipe, more than likely an exhaust valve is not seating, is possibly burned or there is a crack about the valve seat.

You may need to fly the aircraft to the nearest airfield with a maintenance facility. After take-off, reduce the power to a "comfortable" setting for cruise and use a rich mixture setting.

Extremely rough running or vibrating engine after start up

If the engine vibrates excessively after start and the whole instrument panel and aircraft shakes, it is more than likely caused by a stuck exhaust valve. This problem is not as common anymore than in previous years, as most cylinders would have already been upgraded with newer valve guides during the last top overhaul or they would have been replaced. What used to cause the problem was the reduction of lead in the new 100LL AVGAS (LL stands for "Low Lead") and the use of unleaded MOGAS (Car gas/petrol).

First check that the propeller or spinner is not severely damaged, as this may cause the engine to vibrate excessively. However, this should normally show up during your preflight inspection.

Remove the cowling. Remove all the top spark plugs, place your thumb over the spark plug holes at one cylinder at a time and then turn the propeller around in the correct direction until you feel the pressure in the cylinder. Move on to the next cylinder until you find the cylinder that has no or very little compression.

Take a piece of steel wire, securely attach a small nut to the end and position the nut through the spark plug hole between the centre of the open valve head and piston. Rotate the propeller until the piston jams up against the nut. Apply moderate pressure and/or lightly move the propeller back and forth until the valve "snaps" back into its seat and closed position. Problem solved!

An occasional bottle of 'Valve Ease' in each tank, obtainable at most motor spares stores, should help to prevent the problem from occurring again.

Low power, low manifold pressure & low RPM

This can be picked up prior to take-off during a maximum static RPM check or during the take-off roll, as the RPM will be reading lower than normal, however, this is less noticeable on an engine fitted with a constant speed prop. (I personally always monitor my RPM and oil press gauges during take-off, because the take-off is the most critical phase of flight and if anything is not right, this is when you'll notice it.)

There are many possible causes, here are the most common:

- Carburettor ice, accompanied by a rough running engine. – Open carb heat until power is resumed and engine runs smooth again.

- Heavy rain, causing a paper air filter to absorb too much water. – Use carb heat or alt air.

- Poor combustion. – Check compression (blow by).

- Leaks in induction system. – Check induction hoses and especially look for loose hose clamps.

- Faulty carburettor heat system. – Check that the carburettor heat valve is closing and that no hot air is bypassing the valve seals. Rule of thumb: for every 10°F heat above the standard 59°F there is a 1% power loss. At 100°F this adds up to 10% or more power loss.

- Throttle lever may not be reaching full open position. – Check throttle cable, attachments, adjusting screws and links.

- Broken baffles in the muffler can cause blockage and excessive back pressure.

- Cruise propeller fitted or incorrectly adjusted ground adjustable prop – If a "cruise prop" is fitted to an airplane that previously had a finer "climb prop", then you will immediately notice a loss of engine power on take-off. (Normal about 150rpm loss.)

- If your aircraft is fitted with a variable pitch constant speed propeller, check that your engine RPM indicates red line prior to take-off, if it does not, first have the RPM gauge checked for accuracy. If the RPM gauge does not indicate red line, the engine may not be delivering full power and you may need to adjust the constant speed unit (CSU). This can be done by removing the locking wire and by adjusting the governor screw on the CSU. If this still does not correct the situation, the engine should be checked, in particular cylinder compression or "blow bys". If the engine is in good shape, the control arm link may need to be removed and repositioned on the splines of the CSU shaft.

- Turbo charged engines. There are numerous possible problems, here are a few: Controller out of adjustment, damaged turbocharger impeller, waste-gate out of adjustment or stuck open, oil pressure too low to closed waste-gate.

- Inaccurate RPM gauge.

- Worn out spark plugs or incorrect spark gap – replace or re-gap.

- Fuel injected engines - dirty or restricted nozzle.

- Faulty carburettor.

Low power, high oil temp, consumption and CHT

- Possible pre-ignition and detonation! This may quickly result in a hole burning through a piston – Adjust mixture full rich, reduce rpm and lower the nose. Land as soon as possible and shut down.
- Could be caused when using mogas in a high compression engine or an advanced timing.

Low cylinder compression (blow by)

Possible sources of leakage: Exhaust valve, piston rings, intake valve, crack or hole in cylinder head or piston.

To find out where it is leaking use the following tips: Listen in the:

- exhaust for exhaust valve leakage.
- crankcase oil filler for piston ring leakage or piston damage.
- air filter intake for intake valve leakage (first open the throttle).

Pre-ignition

Premature ignition of fuel/air mixture in advance of normal ignition. This is usually caused by a hot spot in the combustion chamber or a magneto cross-fire (burned / cracked distributor in magneto). The hot spot is typically the spark plug electrode or exhaust valve. Check the engine timing and spark plug application. Prolonged operation will result in destruction of piston, cylinder and eventually the entire engine.

Detonation

Detonation is normally caused by using a too low fuel octane or by a magneto timing that may be too far advanced or both! Prolonged operation will result in destruction of piston, cylinder and eventually the entire engine.

Low oil pressure

- Pressure release valve may need adjustment.
- Release valve oil pressure spring may have become weakened or broken. Washers/spacers can be inserted to solve the problem.
- Release valve oil pressure piston and seat may need honing.
- Carbon or metal chips under oil pressure relief valve.
- Incorrect oil viscosity.
- High oil temperature.
- Worn oil pump gears.
- Worn bearings or bearing failure.

Fluctuating oil pressure

Very low, no or fluctuating oil pressure may be a sign of pending catastrophic internal engine damage.

High oil pressure

- Oil relief valve improperly adjusted.
- Improper oil pressure regulator relief spring.
- Improper oil viscosity/weight. This is the most common reason for high oil pressure in cold weather.

High oil temperature

- The engine may be producing too much heat.

- The cooling system may not be working.

- The oil temperature gauge may be inaccurate.

- Magneto timing may be too far advanced.

- Worn out piston rings causing blow by of hot gases heating and causing oil to become black.

High oil consumption

If exceeding maximum oil consumption limit, don't fly the airplane. Oil in the combustion chamber may lower the fuel octane enough to create detonation. Maximum oil consumption limits are in the engine manufacturer's operating manual. Operators of high compression engines should be especially careful about operating with high levels of oil consumption. One quart per hour on a six cylinder low compression engine is one thing, but one quart per hour on a 10:1 compression engine is far too excessive! Engines with high compression pistons should not be allowed to operate with excessive oil consumption.

Reasons for high oil consumption can be the following:

- Improper grade of oil (too low viscosity).

- Failure of new rings to seat properly.

- Failed or failing bearings.

- Worn piston rings and cylinder barrels.

- Worn valve guides.

- Excessive oil leaks.

- Oil siphoning from engine in flight. Insure that oil filter cap is on tight and the oil access door closes properly. Be sure the breather hose is cut properly and located, so there's no chance of siphoning oil from the engine.

- Expander in oil control ring plugged.

- Plugged injector nozzle. The lack of fuel and combustion pressure allows the oil to bypass the piston rings, thereby giving a false impression of ring problems.

- Excessive oil out engine breather. This can be caused by blow-by of combustion gas past the rings.

Oil venting out of crankcase breather tube

- Crankcase pressurization. Check the engine compression. If the oil colour is black and oil temperatures are high, then combustion gases are going into the crankcase.

- Engine breather exposed to low pressure. Ensure that the location of the engine breather is in the precise position as specified by the airframe manufacturer. If the end of the pipe/hose is exposed to airflow in an area of low pressure, it sucks a mist of oil from the crankcase. A remedy is to drill a small hole a few mm/inches further back up the pipe, this will allow air to get sucked in and thus lowering the vacuum in the pipe.

- Oil pressure too high.

Oil turns black

- Blow-by of combustion gases past the piston rings. May also be accompanied by high oil temperature and increased oil flow out engine breather. Check cylinder compressions.

- Excessive oil temperatures.

- Contamination of oil. This is a useful indicator of engine problems. When checking the oil level on the dipstick take notice of the colour of the oil. It will usually be a light tan colour. If it changes to dark black, your engine has a problem.

Oil in combustion chamber (wet piston head)

A cylinder that is not firing will have oil in the combustion chamber. Without proper combustion pressure the rings do not operate properly.

- Worn out piston rings. Glazing of cylinder walls. Inspect cylinder wall for "bore polishing". If the bore is worn smooth so that it shines like a mirror, the rings will allow excessive oil into the combustion chamber. Remove and repair cylinder wall.

- Intake guide. In the Continental C85, O200, C145 & O300 aircraft engine, oil can end up in the induction system and the combustion chamber if an exhaust rocker arm has been installed in the intake position. In these engines only the exhaust rocker arm has an oil squirt. In some engines, if the exhaust rocker arm is mistakenly placed on the intake side, the oil spray may get sucked down the intake guide into the induction system and the combustion chamber.

- Faulty turbocharger: Leaking turbocharger seals. Remove intake tubes and wash out oil. Re-install and run engine for short period. Remove intake tube and see whether oil is travelling from turbo to cylinder or visa versa. Oil in the exhaust system upstream of the turbocharger indicates malfunction such as problems with rings, pistons or valves. If the engine idles too slow, the turbo does not turn allowing oil to leak from the compressor seal.

- Plugged fuel injector nozzle. The lack of fuel and combustion pressure allows the oil to bypass piston rings, thereby giving a false impression of ring problems.

- Cylinder not firing. Check ignition system. Also check for air leak into the induction system.

Oil on spark plug

This may only be evident on the bottom plug and then the piston head will also look wet.

- Poor oil control, most probably past the piston rings. Oil may also suck past the intake guide.

- Poor oil control also occurs when the cylinder bore becomes glazed or polished. The best method of identifying cylinder glazing is by looking at the bore, it should have a slight cross-hatch pattern. If it is shiny like a mirror then it is polished. A polished or glazed bore will allow excessive oil into the combustion chamber.

- Cylinder is not firing. Without normal combustion pressures oil leaks into the combustion chamber.

Cracked spark plug anode insulator

- Dropping the spark plug on the concrete floor. Often this fracture doesn't become evident until the plug is run in an engine.

- Improper gapping procedure. While the insulator in general is very strong, core nose (the part of the insulator visible inside the shell) doesn't tolerate lateral loading very well.

- Excessive torque on installation.

- Insufficient torque on installation.

- Detonation. The extreme cylinder pressures that accompany detonation can cause catastrophic failure of cylinder components, including the core nose of a spark plug. These pressures can also break pistons, resulting in pieces of piston and ring that can impact the core nose and break it. If you see a fractured core nose and other evidence of impact and/or extreme heat, at the very least you'd better take a close look at your pistons, valves, head etc. for damage.

- Pre-ignition, which can either be caused by detonation or can occur on its own, tends to melt things. Usually, the sealant around the electrode and the ceramic melts away.

- Water ingestion leading to a thermal shock to the ceramic. This can be caused by landing in or on water or during very heavy rain, so that water enters the air filter.

- Incorrect spark plug (too hot heat range).

ENGINE MAINTENANCE

Engine oil and oil filter replacement

Aircraft engines that are equipped with a screw on oil filter cartridge should have the engine oil replaced approximately every 50 hours of operation. If the aircraft engine is not equipped with an oil filter and only has an oil screen, the oil should be changed approximately every 25 hours. The oil filter should be replaced every 100 hours and oil screens removed and cleaned. As this is a requirement during a 100 hour inspection you do not need to bother with it.

In the event of you being in a remote part of the bush and no aviation grade oil is available then use a high quality multi-grade motor vehicle engine oil of SAE 20W-50 viscosity or a mono-grade oil of minimum SAE 40 viscosity. Replace the oil filter, drain the oil and replace it with aviation grade oil as soon as possible.

Changing the engine oil

Run engine to warm up the oil, as it flows easier when hot. Remove the cowlings and locate the drain plug at the bottom of the engine oil sump. This could be a "quick drain valve" or just a bolt plug. Cut off the locking wire, remove the plug or connect a hose to the quick drain and push it upwards until it locks in the open position. If the engine only has a bolt plug then use a large funnel, hose or place an oil pan under the engine to capture the oil.

It's a good idea to take a sample of the first 100ml of oil that comes out of the drain and store it for later analysis. However, this by itself will not give you an accurate idea as to what is happening in your engine. It is normal to find a fair amount of metal particles in the first sample that comes out of the sump plug, especially from a newly overhauled engine or cylinders. For a more accurate visual analysis the oil filter should be cut open and inspected. If you choose to send a sample to a lab for microscopic analysis, you will need to take an oil sample by inserting a tube into the sump half way into the oil level through the filler neck and capture some (warm) oil. This is the most accurate oil sample to send for microscopic analysis.

Once all the oil has drained out close the quick drain valve or replace the oil drain plug and tighten it. Take a piece of locking wire and lock the drain plug bolt to the engine case in a manner that will prevent the bolt from turning loose or anticlockwise.

Changing the oil filter

Some older engines don't have external "spin on" oil filters, instead they have an internal oil screen. For those that do have an external oil filter proceed as follows: Cut the locking wire and screw off the oil filter. Drain excess oil from the filter and keep it in a sealed container, so that when convenient, it may be cut open to check for particles in the oil.

Prime the new filter canister by slowly pouring fresh oil into it until it's full and also smear the rubber "O"-ring seal with oil. Screw on the filter canister and hand tighten only. Lock the filter with locking wire to prevent it from becoming loose.

Ground run the engine to check for leaks before replacing the engine cowling and flying.

Air filter maintenance

The air filter should be removed and cleaned every 50 hours. However, in cases where you are operating in extremely dusty conditions, this should be done more frequently than required or every 5 - 10 hours. If not, the engine may not develop maximum horsepower and run rich, as it would not be getting sufficient air into the carburettor.

When operating in a very dusty environment it is advisable to smear a film of grease on the inside of the air intake ducting leading to the carburettor as this will assist in capturing any particles that may escape past a loose or damaged air filter or carburettor heat box valve.

Generally, air filters have either a paper or an oiled sponge element. The paper air filter is more suitable when operating in the bush, as it is easier to clean.

Removing and cleaning an air filter

Unlock the screws around the filter cartridge and remove. Place a clean flat piece of wood, plastic or cardboard on the ground. Hold the filter cartridge with the front intake side facing downwards and lightly but firmly tap the filter up and down. You will notice a fair amount of dirt accumulating on the surface. If you have a paper element filter, before replacing the filter, hold it up to the sun to check it for cleanliness and make sure that there are no bright "pinholes". Pinholes can be repaired by sealing with some silicone sealant.

Filters can also be soaked face down and agitated in a warm, soapy solution to dislodge more stubborn dirt, then rinsed and placed in the sun to dry. Never apply any shock or use compressed air on a paper filter if wet, as this may burst the paper element.

Propeller maintenance and repairs

Inspect the propeller prior to and after every flight, especially when operating in a dusty and rough environment, checking for any sharp nicks and dents in the leading edge of the blades that could lead to a crack. Using a suitable file, carefully file down the rough and sharp spots. If no file is available, a piece of rusty steel pipe or round bar can also work.

FUEL
AVGAS/MOGAS

Caution! Beware of static discharge during refuelling at all times, especially in hot dry climates. Always first ground the container to the aircraft prior to opening and refuelling. Use a large funnel with a good filter screen to refuel.

Many owners and operators of aircraft engines that are designed to use 80-octane AVGAS have switched to using regular automotive fuel, also known as "MOGAS" (MOtor vehicle GASoline) or as "petrol" in some countries.

Besides the economic advantages, many 80-octane aircraft engines actually run better on MOGAS than on 100LL AVGAS. (100 octane Low Lead AViation GASoline).

When operating in some remote parts of the world, AVGAS is not always available. Fortunately, many GA aircraft are approved by a Supplemental Type Certificate (STC) to run on regular unleaded MOGAS. However, although at the time of writing this book, there was no ethanol in fuel in Southern Africa, care should be taken when purchasing MOGAS from a small service station out in the back-country and should be tested prior to use. Gasoline blended with ethanol is corrosive and attacks fuel systems, not only the rubber components, but aluminium, too. If you cannot find gasoline that you are certain is ethanol free, you must revert to using AVGAS until non-ethanol automotive gasoline can be obtained.

Fuels containing ethanol may not legally be used in aircraft engines, however, in an emergency you could do so, but should drain it out and fill up with AVGAS or MOGAS as soon as possible afterwards.

Octane rating vs Compression Ratio (CR)

I do not recommend MOGAS to be used in a typical "old design" aircraft piston engine, where the compression ratio exceeds 8:1. Most aircraft piston engines approved for using regular octane MOGAS are all 7:1 − 7.5:1 CR normally aspirated (carburettor) engines. Once these engines are modified by replacing the low compression pistons with pistons of a higher compression ratio, great care must be taken to ensure that you use only the highest octane rating possible at all times and that the magneto timing is set correctly to limit the chances of detonation! The higher the compression ratio, the higher the octane rating or "anti-knock" index requirement.

Testing fuel for ethanol, water and cleanliness

Test the fuel for cleanliness, odour and colour the same way you normally do during a pre-flight inspection. During pre-flight always drain and check fuel from the filter, which is normally located at a position lower than the engine. If you do not already have a fuel tester calibrated for testing for alcohol in fuel, you can fabricate one as follows:

On a test tube or fuel tester bottle, make a permanent line about an inch (25mm) from the bottom. Fill with water to this line and then fill the tube to the top with gasoline. Cover the tube, agitate it, then let it stand.

Ethanol mixes with water, therefore, after mixing the water and the gasoline, if the water level appears to have increased, then the fuel contains ethanol and should not be used.

Ethanol fuels can damage the rubber and aluminium components of the typical aircraft fuel system. Ethanol increases the volatility of fuel and hence the possibility of vapor lock also increases. Ethanol may vent off at altitude, reducing both range and octane. For these reasons fuel containing ethanol should never be used in aircraft piston engines.

It is, however, interesting to note that an aircraft engine may run very well on pure ethanol and even produce more horse power with an even lower risk of detonation than when using AVGAS.

Part 2. Turbine-propeller (turboprop) engine

A turboprop engine is a turbine engine that drives a propeller through a reduction gearbox. The exhaust gases drive a power turbine connected by a shaft that drives the reduction gear assembly. Reduction gearing is necessary in turboprop engines, because optimum propeller performance is achieved at much slower speeds than the engine's operating RPM. Turboprop engines are a compromise between turbojet engines and reciprocating powerplants. Turboprop engines are most efficient at speeds between 250 and 400 mph and altitudes between 18,000 and 30,000 feet. They also perform well at the slow airspeeds required for takeoff and landing and are fuel efficient.

Components of a turbine engine

The basic principle of the turbine engine is identical to the reciprocating engine.

1. The four basic steps for any internal combustion engine are:
2. Intake of air and fuel.
3. Compression of the air and fuel mixture.
4. Combustion where fuel is injected (if it was not drawn in with the intake air) and burned to convert the stored energy.
5. Expansion and exhaust where the converted energy is put to use.

These principles are also exactly the same ones used to make an aircraft piston or car engine run.

In the case of a piston engine, the intake, compression, combustion and exhaust steps occur in the same place (the cylinder head) at different times as the piston goes up and down. In the turbine engine these same four steps occur at the same time, but in different places.

As a result of this fundamental difference, the turbine engine sections are called:

1. inlet section,
2. compressor section,
3. combustion section,
4. exhaust section.

The inlet and compressor sections are referred to as the "cold section" and the combustion and exhaust sections are referred to as the "hot section".

There are two types of turboprop engines, the "fixed shaft" and the "split shaft" or "free turbine". I will only describe the free turbine engine such as the Walter M601 and the Pratt & Whitney PT-6, as these are the most common engines fitted to aircraft involved in bush flying operations.

Split Shaft / Free Turbine Engine

In a free power-turbine engine, the propeller is driven by a separate turbine through reduction gearing. The propeller is not on the same shaft as the basic engine turbine and compressor *(see figure 18)*.

Unlike the fixed shaft engine, in the split shaft engine the propeller can be feathered in flight or on the ground with the basic engine still running. This facilitates fast passenger loading and permits very quiet ground operation. The free power-turbine design allows the pilot to select a desired propeller governing RPM, regardless of basic engine RPM. Propeller RPM can be varied in flight permitting propeller RPM to be set for quieter cruise and optimum efficiency. During an engine start, only the compressor section of the engine needs to be rotated by the starter-generator. By comparison, a fixed-shaft engine must spin all rotating components including the reduction gearbox and propeller during an engine start, resulting in a requirement for heavier starting systems.

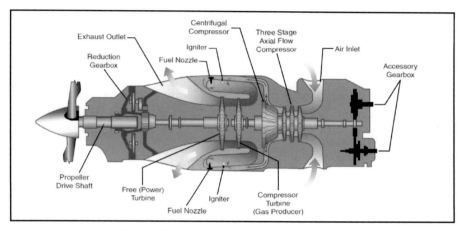

Figure 18. Split shaft/free turbine engine.

A typical free power-turbine engine has two independent counter-rotating turbines. One turbine drives the compressor, while the other drives the propeller through a reduction gearbox. The compressor in the basic engine normally consists of three or four axial flow compressor stages combined with a single centrifugal compressor stage. The axial and centrifugal stages are assembled on the same shaft and operate as a single unit.

Inlet air enters the engine via a circular plenum near the rear of the engine and flows forward through the successive compressor stages. The flow is directed outward by the centrifugal compressor stage through radial diffusers before entering the combustion chamber, where the flow direction is actually reversed.

In the combustion chamber the air is mixed with fuel and burned. Igniter plugs are used to light the fuel/air mixture when the engine is started. They are not required to maintain the combustion process and are shut off once the engine has reached idle speed. The expanding hot gases are directed first through the compressor turbine and then through the power turbine. A shaft from the power turbine drives the propeller reduction gearbox.

After leaving the power turbine, the gases are collected in an exhaust scroll, then discharged to the atmosphere through two exhaust stacks near the front of the engine. On a single engined turbine aircraft these exhaust stacks are usually positioned in such a way as to enable the thrust of the exhaust to counteract the propeller torque. It is for this reason, that when you observe a single engined turbine aircraft from the front, you notice the exhaust stacks are positioned at different angles.

A pneumatic fuel control system controls fuel flow to maintain the power set by the power lever.

Except in the beta range, propeller speed within the governing range remains constant at any selected propeller control lever position through the action of a propeller governor.

The accessory drive at the aft end of the engine provides power to drive fuel pumps, fuel control, oil pumps, a starter/generator, and a tachometer (RPM) transmitter. At this point, the speed of the drive (N1/ng) is the true speed of the compressor side of the engine, approximately 37,500 RPM.

Power plant (engine and propeller) operation is achieved by three sets of controls for each engine: the power lever, propeller lever and condition lever *(see photo 52).* The power lever serves to control engine power in the range from idle through take-off power. Forward or aft motion of the power lever increases or decreases gas generator RPM (N1/ng) and thereby increases or decreases engine power. The propeller lever is operated conventionally and controls the constant-speed propellers through the primary governor.

The propeller RPM range is normally from 1,500 to 2000. The condition lever controls the flow of fuel to the engine. Like the mixture lever in a piston-powered airplane, the condition lever is located at the far right of the power quadrant, however, the condition lever on a turboprop engine is really just an on/off valve for delivering fuel. There are "High Idle" and "Low Idle" positions for ground operations, but condition levers have no metering function. Leaning is not required in turbine engines, this function is performed automatically by a dedicated fuel control unit.

52. Powerplant (engine and propeller)controls.

**ITT
(interstage turbine temperature)
indicator**

Torque-meter

Propeller tachometer

**N1
(gas generator)
tachometer**

Fuel flow indicator

**Oil temperature /
pressure indicator**

53. Engine instruments – split shaft / free turbine engine.

Engine instruments in a split shaft/free turbine engine typically consist of the following basic indicators *(see photo 50)*:

• ITT (interstage turbine temperature) indicator,
• Torque-meter,
• Propeller tachometer,
• N1 (gas generator) tachometer,
• Fuel flow indicator,
• Oil temperature/pressure indicator.

The ITT indicator gives an instantaneous reading of engine gas temperature between the compressor turbine and the power turbines (Interstage). The torque-meter responds to power lever movement and gives an indication (in foot-pounds (ft/lb)) of the torque being applied to the propeller. Because the propeller is not attached physically to the shaft of the free gas turbine engine, two tachometers are justified, one for the propeller and one for the gas generator. The propeller tachometer is read directly in revolutions per minute. The N1/ng or gas generator is read in percent of RPM. In the Pratt & Whitney PT-6 engine it is based on a figure of 37,000 RPM at 100 percent. Maximum continuous gas generator is limited to 38,100 RPM or 101.5 percent N1.

The ITT indicator and torque-meter are used to set take-off power. Climb and cruise power are established with the torque-meter and propeller tachometer while observing ITT limits. Gas generator (N1) operation is monitored by the gas generator tachometer. Proper observation and interpretation of these instruments provide an indication of engine performance and condition.

TURBINE ENGINE OPERATIONAL CONSIDERATIONS

Operational considerations common to all turbine engines are engine temperature limits, foreign object damage, hot start, compressor stall and flame out.

All turbine engines, turboprop or turbojet, operation is limited by temperatures, rotational speeds, and (in the case of turboprops or turboshafts) torque. Depending on the installation, the primary parameter for power setting might be temperature, torque, fuel flow or RPM (either propeller RPM, gas generator (compressor) RPM or both). In cold weather conditions, torque limits can be exceeded, while temperature limits are still within acceptable range. While in hot weather conditions, temperature limits may be exceeded without exceeding torque limits. In any weather, the maximum power setting of a turbine engine is usually obtained with the throttle positioned somewhat aft of the full forward position. The transitioning pilot must understand the importance of knowing and observing limits on turbine engines. An over temp or over torque condition that lasts for more than a few seconds can destroy internal engine components.

Engine Temperature Limitations

A major limiting factor in a gas turbine engine is the temperature of the turbine section. The temperature of a turbine section must be monitored closely to prevent overheating the turbine blades and other exhaust section components. One common way of monitoring the temperature of a turbine section is with an EGT gauge. EGT is an engine operating limit used to monitor overall engine operating conditions.

Variations of EGT systems bear different names based on the location of the temperature sensors. Common turbine temperature sensing gauges include the turbine inlet temperature (TIT) gauge, turbine outlet temperature (TOT) gauge, inter-stage turbine temperature (ITT) gauge and the turbine gas temperature (TGT) gauge.

ITT indicator

The highest temperature in any turbine engine occurs at the turbine inlet in the inter-stage section. Therefore the Inter Turbine Temperature indicator (ITT) is usually the main limiting factor in turbine engine operation.

Torque-meter

Turboprop/turboshaft engine power output is measured by the torque-meter. Torque is a twisting force applied to a shaft. The torque-meter measures power applied to the shaft. Turboprop and turbo-shaft engines are designed to produce torque for driving a propeller. Torque-meters are calibrated in percentage units, foot-pounds or psi.

NP indicator

NP refers to the RPM of the propeller shaft. Depending on the design of the propeller, the red line would be about 2000 RPM.

N1 / ng Indicator

"N1" or "ng" represents the rotational speed of the low pressure compressor and is presented on the indicator as a percentage of design rpm. After start, the speed of the low pressure compressor is governed by the N1/ng turbine wheel. The N1/ng turbine wheel is connected to the low pressure compressor through a concentric shaft.

N2 / nf Indicator

"N2" or "nf" represents the rotational speed of the high pressure compressor and is presented on the indicator as a percentage of design rpm. The high pressure compressor is governed by the N2 / nf turbine wheel. The N2/nf turbine wheel is connected to the high pressure compressor through a concentric shaft.

Definition of "N" & "n"

"N" or "ng" is the abbreviation that describes the RPM of a turbine engine. "N1"or "ng" & "N2" or "nf" refers to the speed of the gas generator (gas producer) section (RPM). Each engine manufacturer will pick between those two abbreviations, however, "N" is most common.

The International System of Units was developed in an effort to standardize measurement in scientific circles. The "SI" system represents a modern form of the metric system. "N" stands for "Newton" and is the SI symbol that represents Force, Thrust and Tension. The SI unit of force, the Newton, is defined to be the force that accelerates a mass of one kilogram at the rate of one meter per second. This means the newton is equal to one kilogram meter per second squared, so the algebraic relationship is $N = kgms^{-2}$.

The generally accepted SI symbol for rotational frequency is "n". Rotational frequency is normally expressed in "radians per second". "n" rotational speeds in turbine engines are predetermined maximum rotational speeds of specific shafts. Indicated rotational frequency is typically expressed in percent of "n".

Reverse Thrust and Beta Range Operations

The thrust that a propeller provides is a function of the angle of attack at which the air strikes the blades and the speed at which this occurs. The angle of attack varies with the pitch angle of the propeller.

The so called "flat pitch" is the blade position offering minimum resistance to rotation and no net thrust for moving the airplane. Forward pitch produces forward thrust, higher pitch angles are required at higher airplane speeds.

The "feathered" position is the highest pitch angle obtainable. The feathered position produces no forward thrust. The propeller is generally placed in feather only in case of in-flight engine failure, to minimize drag and prevent the air from using the propeller as a turbine.

In the "reverse" pitch position, the engine/propeller turns in the same direction as in the normal (forward) pitch position, but the propeller blade angle is positioned to the other side of flat pitch. In reverse pitch, air is pushed away from the airplane rather than being drawn over it. Reverse pitch results in braking action, rather than forward thrust of the airplane. It is used for backing away from obstacles when taxiing, controlling taxi speed or to aid in bringing the airplane to a stop during the landing roll. Reverse pitch does not mean reverse rotation of the engine. The engine delivers power just the same, no matter which side of flat pitch the propeller blades are positioned.

With a turboprop engine, in order to obtain enough power for flight, the power lever is placed somewhere between flight idle (also referred to as "high idle") and maximum. The power lever directs a fuel control unit to manually select fuel. The propeller governor selects the propeller pitch needed to keep the propeller/engine on speed. This is referred to as the propeller governing or "Alpha" mode of operation. When positioned aft of flight idle, however, the power lever directly controls the propeller blade angle. This is known as the "Beta" range of operation.

The beta range of operation consists of power lever positions from flight idle to maximum reverse.

Beginning at power lever positions just aft of flight idle, propeller blade pitch angles become progressively flatter with aft movement of the power lever until they go beyond maximum flat pitch and into negative pitch, resulting in reverse thrust. While in a fixed shaft/ constant-speed engine, the engine speed remains largely unchanged as the propeller blade angles achieve their negative values. On the split shaft engine, as the negative 5° position is reached, further aft movement of the power lever will also result in a progressive increase in engine (N1/ng) RPM until a maximum value of about negative 11° of blade angle and 85 percent N1/ng are achieved.

Operating in the beta range and/or with reverse thrust requires specific techniques and procedures depending on the particular airplane make and model. There are also specific engine parameters and limitations for operations within this area that must be adhered to. It is essential that a pilot transitioning to turboprop airplanes become knowledgeable and proficient in these areas, which are unique to turbine-engine powered airplanes, especially twin-engine airplanes operated in a STOL environment.

It is normally prohibited to use Beta mode at any time during flight in twin-engine turbine airplanes. However, this mode is sometimes used in ground effect just prior to touchdown during an extreme short field landing in a one-way-in-one-way-out strip, then on touchdown full reverse thrust is selected.

Starting the turbine engine

To start the engine, the compressor section is rotated by an electrical starter (which is also the generator) on small engines or an air driven starter on large engines. As compressor RPM accelerates, air is brought in through the inlet duct, compressed to a high pressure, and delivered to the combustion section (combustion chamber). Fuel is then injected by a fuel controller through spray nozzles and ignited by igniter plugs. (Not all of the compressed air is used to support combustion. Some of the compressed air bypasses the burner section and circulates within the engine to provide internal cooling.) The fuel/air mixture in the combustion chamber is then burned in a continuous combustion process and produces a very high temperature, typically around 4,000°F, which heats the entire air mass to 1,600 – 2,400°F. The mixture of hot air and gases expands and is directed to the turbine blades forcing the turbine section to rotate, which in turn drives the compressor by means of a direct shaft. After powering the turbine section, the high velocity excess exhaust exits the tail pipe or exhaust section. Once the turbine section is powered by gases from the burner section, the starter is disengaged, and the igniters are turned off. Combustion continues until the engine is shut down by turning off the fuel supply.

Typical start procedure:

- electrical switches and circuit breakers on as required;
- fuel shut-off valve closed, power lever at idle, propeller lever at feather, condition lever at low or ground idle;
- check voltage is sufficient for start;
- ignitors on;
- starter on;
- apx 20% N1 – open fuel shut-off valve and monitor the ITT and oil pressure;
- apx 40% N1 - starter and ignitors off, generator on;
- set Propeller lever to fine pitch;
- apx 60% N1 - engine is at ground idle.

Fuels

A big advantage of turbine engines, especially in remote parts, is that they can run on just about any available fuel.

The PT6A engine for example is approved for operation with all commercial jet fuels, JP-4, JP-5, "Jet-A" and for a maximum of 150 hours during any overhaul period with all grades of aviation gasoline

(AVGAS). It will also run just fine on regular MOGAS! Specific grades of diesel fuel are also approved as alternate fuels for restricted use.

No engine adjustments are required in changing from one fuel to another, nor is it necessary to purge the fuel system when changing fuels, except when using alternate fuels. The engine will run fine on a mixture of various fuels. There are, however, some restrictions in the POH as to how long the engine may be run on any particular type of fuel and the engine power or torque may be slightly reduced due to temperatures.

ENGINE MALFUNCTIONS & DIAGNOSTICS

To provide effective understanding of and preparation for the correct responses and diagnosis of engine problems, this section will describe turboprop engine malfunctions and their consequences in a manner that is applicable to turboprop engines.

Starting problems
No RPM (N1) during start attempt

- No electrical power to starter. Check circuit breaker.

- Starter shaft sheared and starter only spins. Remove to repair or replace.

- Starter shaft spline work out and starter only spins. Remove to repair or replace.

- No N1 indication. Check if oil pressure is rising. Could be defective N1 indicator or tach drive.

- N1 rotor system seized. Remove starter-generator and attempt to turn drive.

Insufficient N1 RPM during start

- Insufficient voltage to starter. Check batteries, power source and leads.

- N1 RPM indicating system may be faulty.

- Check N1 rotor system for rubbing, check clearance. If okay, the compressor is rubbing.

N1 RPM excessively high with rapid acceleration

- Accessory gearbox input shaft may be disconnected. Danger exists of an over-temp during start.

Delayed start

- Improper start technique.

- A low voltage may be accompanied with low cranking RPM and this can cause a hot start.

- Fuel nozzle restricted. Remove, inspect and clean or replace as necessary.

- Air in the fuel system. Bleed the system. Check for reason for air entering the system.

- Check igniters and replace if necessary.

- Check ignition exciter/s. If possible, check for ignition while dry motoring.

Fuel fails to ignite

- Improper start technique, possibly too early disengaging of starter. Could cause hotter than normal start.

- Fuel topping governor faulty.

- Corrosion or ice in FCU bellows section.

- Contaminated or defective FCU. Check all fuel filters. Check FCU bypass valve.

- Minimum fuel flow stop set too low. Check minimum fuel flow. Remove the Py line from prop governor or fuel topping governor and leave open. Perform normal start and check N1 RPM.

Hot/hung start

When the EGT exceeds the safe limit it experiences a "hot start". It is caused by too much fuel entering the combustion chamber or insufficient turbine rpm. Any time an engine has a hot start, refer to the AFM/POH or an appropriate maintenance manual for inspection requirements.

If the engine fails to accelerate to the proper speed after ignition or does not accelerate to idle RPM, a hung or false start has occurred.

Possible causes:

- Improper start technique. Possibly caused by entering fuel too early and/or disengaging the starter motor too early.

- Insufficient voltage to the starter causing lower than normal cranking RPM and loss of starter assist.

- Faulty starter.

- Engine bleed air open or leaking. Blank the engine bleed air port and try again.

- Delayed igniters. Check ignition and exciter circuits.

- Fuel nozzle restriction. Check fuel nozzles.

- Start control transfer valve stuck open. Remove and clean valve.

- Dump valve in flow divider stuck closed. This will not allow fuel to dump.

- Defective N1 indicator possibly reading high resulting in too early entry of fuel.

Engine operating malfunctions

Propeller overspeed (N2)

- Defective prop RPM indicator.

- Defective prop governor. Check setting.

- Defective prop or fuel topping governors.

- Defective overspeed governor.

- Binding or disconnected rigging.

Compressor overspeed (N1)

- Sheared FCU drive coupling.

- Defective FCU bypass diaphragm.

- FCU bypass valve stuck closed.

Propeller slow to feather

- Defective prop governor or rigging incorrect.

- Binding of a propeller component.

Propeller slow to unfeather or fails to unfeather

- Prop shaft transfer housing seals leaking.

- Transfer bobbin seals leaking.

- Defective prop governor. Check rigging and setting.

- Defective overspeed governor. Check rigging and setting.

- Obstructed prop shaft oil passage.

- Binding of a propeller component.

High fuel flow

- Defective indicating system.

- Defective or incorrectly rigged or adjusted compressor bleed valve. If it is not closing properly, it may cause ITT and N1 RPM to be higher than normal.

- Compressor air leaks. Check all gaskets on gas generator case.

Vibration

- Prop out of balance. Check prop for damage, blade angle and twist.

- Compressor out of balance (steady humming sound). Check for FOD. Check bleed valve for being stuck shut. May cause higher than normal ITT at idle.

- Compressor out of balance (intermittent hooting sound). This condition is acceptable if hooting sound goes away at about 60% N1 RPM. Turbine balance should be checked.

- Power turbine may be out of balance. Have turbine checked for balance and damage.

High N1 RPM

- Check indicating system.

- Compressor dirty. Perform compressor wash.

- Compressor FOD. Check first stage blades for FOD.

- Compressor bleed valve(s) open. May also cause high ITT.

- Excessive gas generator air leaks. Check all gas generator gaskets for integrity and security.

Uncontrolled acceleration

- FCU drive sheared.
- FCU bypass diaphram ruptured.
- FCU bypass valve stuck closed.

Stall during acceleration (shotgun sound)

- Faulty compressor bleed valve.
- Faulty FCU.
- Compressor FOD. Check first stage compressor blades for FOD.

Failure to accelerate properly

- Sensor line restricted or leaking.
- Corrosion or ice in FCU bellows section.
- Defective FCU.
- Dirt in pneumatic section of FCU.
- Contaminated P3 filter. This will also cause a slow start.

Failure to decelerate

- Disconnected or improperly rigged FCU.
- FCU bypass valve stuck.
- Binding control linkage.

Flame-out

- Interrupted fuel supply. Possibly fuel valve inadvertently shut off.
- Fuel pump failure.
- Air in fuel system may cause a flame-out at idle after a start. Bleed fuel system. Check reason for air entering fuel system.

- Contaminated FCU. Check all fuel filters. Clean fuel system and replace filters as necessary.

Incorrect idle speed

- Incorrect idle setting.
- Minimum fuel flow stop setting too high. Will not decrease to idle fuel flow.
- Air leak in signal lines. Check lines for cracks and security.
- FCU control rod will not return to idle position.

Overtemp (above red line)

- Faulty gauge or sensor.
- Excessive accessory loading. Turn off generator and recheck.
- Torque indication low. Possibly a faulty torque-meter or sensor.

Low N1 RPM and high T5

- Hot section distress. Engine needs a hot section inspection.

Low oil pressure

- Low oil level. Check the tank oil level. Check oil consumption.
- Defective oil pressure indication.
- Pressure relief valve malfunctioning, probably stuck open.
- Internal oil leak will cause oil smoke on start or shut down and oil smell in cabin area.

- Failed heat shield in power section causes excessive heating of oil. Oil cooler may not be able to handle the added temperature.

High oil pressure

- Defective oil pressure gauge or sensor.
- Pressure relief valve malfunctioning.

High oil temperature

- Insufficient oil supply. Check oil tank level. Replenish supply, check consumption.
- Defective cooling system. Check oil cooler and thermostat.
- Excessive idling in feather will reduce air volume to oil cooler.
- Failed heat shield in power section will cause excessive heating of oil.

Excessive oil consumption

- Oil leak.
- System over serviced. Oil level too high.
- Restriction in scavenge tubes. Will result in inability to scavenge oil and cause bearing area flooding.
- Defective packing / gaskets on oil filter housing or oil tank. Check packings / gaskets.
- Clogged scavenge screen in rear case. Check main oil filter for carbon.
- Defective oil seals. Check inlet and exhaust for oil.

- Oil to fuel heater leak. Oil leaking into fuel system and is being burned off.
- Oil from breather excessive. Defective carbon seal.
- Defective oil filter check valve. Will allow oil to migrate to pressure system over flowing into bearing areas.

High breather discharge

- Overfilled oil system.
- Breather carbon seal defective.
- Excessive back pressure in scavenge system. Check scavenge tubes, oil lines and oil cooler for restriction.

Fluctuating oil pressure

- Insufficient oil supply. Replenish supply and check consumption.
- Defective indication. Loose wire.
- Restricted oil filter. Pressure release valve bypassing. Check oil filter. Debris may have clogged oil vanes.
- Pressure relief valve sticking. Clean, re-face/polish valve.

Thrust variations

Turbine engine thrust varies directly with air density. As air density decreases, so does thrust. Additionally, because air density decreases with an increase in temperature, increased temperatures will also result in decreased thrust. While both, turbine and reciprocating powered engines, are affected to some degree by high relative humidity, turbine engines will experience a negligible loss of thrust, while reciprocating engines a significant loss of brake horsepower.

Foreign Object Damage (FOD)

Due to the design and function of a turbine engine's air inlet, the possibility of ingestion of debris always exists. This causes significant damage, particularly to the compressor and turbine sections. When ingestion of debris occurs, it is called foreign object damage (FOD). Typical FOD consists of small nicks and dents, caused by ingestion of small objects from the ramp, taxiway or runway, but FOD caused by bird strikes or ice ingestion also occurs. Sometimes FOD results in total destruction of an engine.

Prevention of FOD is a high priority. Some engine inlets have a tendency to form a vortex between the ground and the inlet during ground operations. A vortex dissipater may be installed on these engines. Other devices, such as screens and/or deflectors, may also be utilized. Pre-flight procedures include a visual inspection for any sign of FOD.

In-flight engine operating malfunctions

Vibration

Vibration could result from a wide variety of engine conditions. Engine vibration may be caused by propeller unbalance (ice build up, blade material loss due to ingested material or blade distortion due to FOD) or by an internal engine failure. It is not easy to identify the cause of the vibration from inside the aircraft. Although the vibration from some failures may feel very severe, it may not necessarily cause damage to the engine mounts or airframe. Reference to the engine gauges will help to establish whether an actual failure exists.

Compressor stalls

Compressor blades are small airfoils and are subject to the same aerodynamic principles that apply to any airfoil. A compressor blade has an angle of attack, which is a result of inlet air velocity and the compressor's rotational velocity. These two forces combine to form a vector, which defines the airfoil's actual angle of attack to the approaching inlet air.

A compressor stall is an imbalance between inlet velocity and compressor rotational speed. Compressor stalls occur when the compressor blade's angle of attack exceeds the critical angle of attack. At this point, smooth airflow is interrupted and turbulence is created with pressure fluctuations. Compressor stalls cause air flowing in the compressor to slow down and stagnate, sometimes reversing direction.

Compressor stalls can be transient and intermittent or steady and severe. Indications of a transient/intermittent stall are usually an intermittent "bang", as backfire and flow reversal take place. If the stall develops and becomes steady, strong vibration and a loud roar may develop from the continuous flow reversal. Often, engine gauges do not show a mild or transient stall, but they do indicate a developed stall. Typical instrument indications include fluctuations in RPM and an increase in exhaust gas temperature. Most transient stalls are not harmful to the engine and often correct themselves after one or two pulsations. The possibility of severe engine damage from a steady state stall is immediate. Recovery must be accomplished by quickly reducing power, decreasing the aircraft's angle of attack and increasing the airspeed.

Although all gas turbine engines are subject to compressor stalls, most models have systems that inhibit them. Automatic bleed air from the compressor prevents compressor stall during acceleration from low engine speeds or deceleration from high engine speeds. Another system uses a variable inlet guide vane (VIGV) and variable stator vanes, which direct the incoming air into the rotor blades at an appropriate angle.

Flameout

A flameout occurs when the fire in a turbine engine unintentionally goes out. If the rich limit of the fuel/air ratio is exceeded in the combustion chamber, the flame will blow out. This condition is often referred to as a rich flameout. It generally results from very fast engine acceleration, in which an overly rich mixture causes the fuel temperature to drop below the combustion temperature. It may also be caused by insufficient airflow to support combustion. A flameout will be accompanied by an ignition light, drop in ITT, torque, engine core speed and in engine pressure ratio (EPR).

A more common flameout occurrence is due to low fuel pressure and low engine speeds, which typically are associated with high-altitude flight. This situation may also occur with the engine throttled back during a descent, which can set up the lean-condition flameout. A weak mixture can easily cause the flame to die out, even with a normal airflow through the engine. Any interruption of the fuel supply can result in a flameout. This may be due to prolonged unusual attitudes, such as a malfunctioning fuel control system, turbulence, icing, severe inclement weather, a volcanic ash encounter or running out of fuel. A flameout at take-off power is unusual – only about 10% of flameouts occur at take-off power.

Symptoms of a flameout normally are the same as those following an engine failure. If the flameout is due to a transitory condition, such as an imbalance between fuel flow and engine speed, an airstart may be attempted once the condition is corrected.

Fuel leaks

Major leaks in the fuel system are a concern to the flight crew, because they may result in engine fire or, eventually, in fuel exhaustion. A very large leak can produce engine flameout. Engine instruments will only indicate a leak if it is downstream of the fuel flowmeter. A leak between the tanks and the fuel flowmeter can only be recognized by comparing fuel usage between engines, by comparing actual usage to planned usage or by visual inspection for fuel flowing out of the pylon or cowlings.

In the event of a major leak, the crew should consider whether the leak needs to be isolated to prevent fuel exhaustion.

It should be noted that the likelihood of fire resulting from such a leak is greater at low altitude, even if no fire is observed in flight it is advisable for emergency services to be available upon landing.

Fuel filter clogging

Fuel filter clogging can result from the failure of one of the fuel tank boost pumps (the pump generates debris which is swept downstream to the fuel filter), from severe contamination of the fuel tanks during maintenance (scraps of rag, sealant etc., that are swept downstream to the fuel filter) or, more seriously, from gross contamination of the fuel.

Fuel filter clogging will usually be seen at high-power settings, when the fuel flow through the filter (and the sensed pressure drop across the filter) is greatest. If multiple fuel-filter bypass indications are seen, the fuel may be heavily contaminated with water, rust, algae etc. Once the filters bypass and the contaminant goes straight into the engine fuel system, the engine fuel control may no longer operate as intended and then there is a danger of flameout.

Oil system problems

The engine oil system has a relatively large number of indicated parameters (pressure, temperature, quantity, filter clogging). Many of the sensors used are subject to giving false indications, especially on earlier engine models. Multiple abnormal system indications confirm a genuine failure. A single abnormal indication may or may not be a valid indication of failure.

There is considerable variation between failure progressions in the oil system, so the symptoms given below may vary from case to case.

Oil system problems may appear at any flight phase and generally progress gradually. They may eventually lead to severe engine damage if the engine is not shut down.

Oil leaks

Leaks will produce a sustained reduction in oil quantity, down to zero (though there will still be some usable oil in the system at this point). Once the oil is completely exhausted, oil pressure will drop to zero, followed by the low oil pressure light. There have been cases where maintenance error caused leaks on multiple engines. It is therefore advisable to monitor the oil quantity carefully on the good engines as well. Rapid change in the oil quantity after power lever movement may not indicate a leak, it may be due to oil "gulping" or "hiding", as more oil flows into the sumps.

Bearing failures

Bearing failures will be accompanied by an increase in oil temperature and indicated vibration. If a chip detector light is installed, it may come on. Audible noises and filter clog messages may follow. If the failure progresses to severe engine damage, it may be accompanied by low oil quantity and pressure indications.

Oil pump failures

Oil pump failure will be accompanied by low indicated oil pressure and a low oil pressure light or by an oil filter clog message. For propellers that use engine oil pressure for actuation, the propeller will pitchlock or move to feather.

Oil system contamination

Contamination of the oil system due to carbon deposits, cotton waste, improper fluids etc. will generally lead to an oil filter clog indication or an impending bypass indication.

This indication may disappear if thrust is reduced, since the oil flow and pressure differential across the filter will also drop.

Part 3. Airframe maintenance and repairs

Tyre and landing gear repairs and maintenance

Light bush planes are normally equipped with oversize high floatation tyres between 8.00 X 6" and 9.00 X 6". These tyres should never be over inflated or they will not do what they are designed for. In addition they will wear out very quickly. If running very low pressures, make a chalk or paint line on the tyre wall and wheel rim and check this line during every pre- and post-flight. If the lines do not line up, the tyres are rotating on the rim and the pressure is too low or you are applying too heavy breaking.

Pressure

Prior to departing from a low elevation airstrip, such as at the coast, to fly to a much higher elevation airstrip, it is best to first deflate these tyres by about 20% to prevent them from becoming too hard, possibly leading to a blow-out on landing.

Punctures

Simply inflating the tyre with a commonly available aerosol tyre puncture sealer can temporarily repair most minor tyre punctures. Never fly without one of these. However, first try to remove the object causing the puncture. One can is sufficient for multiple inflations. Clean out the tube as soon as possible after using an aerosol tyre repair as its contents are corrosive.

In the event of a more serious puncture, remove the wheel, split the rim, remove the tube and repair using your tyre repair kit.

Oleo collapse

In the event of an oleo collapse take a 3-4 inch/75-100mm piece of rubber or PVC hose, cut it open lengthwise and clamp it around the oleo shaft with hose clamps.

Loss of brake pressure

If it is necessary to top up the hydraulic break fluid reservoir and no aviation grade hydraulic fluid is available, then normal automotive "Automatic Transmission Fluid" (ATF) will work. DO NOT USE automotive brake fluid, unless specified in the POH.

Bleeding the brake system can be done by filling up the reservoir, that is normally located behind or close to the pedals and then loosening the nipple underneath the slave cylinder on the wheel allowing fluid to run out into a container. A slight amount of pressure on the pedal will assist in getting any air out of the lines. Do not allow the reservoir to run dry, otherwise you will have to start all over again.

An easier way of bleeding the brake system is using an oil can that has a built in pump action. Ensure that there are no air bubbles in the flexible tube attached to the oil can, then attach the end of the tube to the nipple on the slave cylinder and simply pump the fluid up the line until the reservoir over flows. The system should now be bled.

Wings & fuselage repairs

In general, any minor dents in the fuselage and leading edges of the wings that have not led to any contact or damage to the spar, struts or other major structural components and attachment points may be acceptable and can easily be "reformed" and taped up.

It is of utmost importance to perform a thorough inspection of the aircraft. Remove inspection covers and examine all attachment points and bolts. Carefully examine the aircraft from all angles for any sign that seems odd or out of shape. Check for skin creasing and rivet shearing. Vigorously move the wings about whilst observing the surfaces for any sign of bending, creasing or buckling. Check for full and free movement of all controls.

Windshield: cleaning and repairs

Always remember that light aircraft windshields and windows are made of a plastic material. If possible, use warm soapy water and your bare hand to clean whilst feeling for grit and bugs etc. Then use a clean soft cloth or sponge dedicated for cleaning the windshield only. Do not dry off with a cloth, rather just pour clean water over to rinse off the soap. If the water leaves marks on the windshield, then only a very clean chamois should be used to dry the windshield.

Remember that every time you wipe the windshield, there is a very good chance that scratches will occur.

If possible, use a good quality "Perspex"/"Plexiglass" polish to treat the windshield. Regular aerosol furniture polish works very well, too. Preferably choose a product that advertises "suitable for clear plastic/Perspex".

Never place headphones or GPS etc. on top of the instrument panel, as these items will scratch the windshield in the most critical viewing area (3-4" above panel) and it is very difficult to remove scratches in this area on the inside of a windshield.

Removing scratches

Scratches on a "Perspex"/"Plexiglass" windshield or window can easily be removed with a little brass or silver polish, using a soft damp cloth.

Repairing a broken windshield

A cracked or broken windshield or window can be temporarily repaired by using a strong duct or gaffer tape that you should always carry in your toolbox. Suitable glue may also be an advantage to add extra strength to the repair. Another method is to drill small holes all around the broken pieces and wire stitch the pieces together. However, this requires a small drill and a fair amount of thin steel or locking wire.

Part 4. Electrical and avionics, fault diagnostics and repairs

Typical piston engine aircraft electrical systems are 12-24 volt direct current (DC), which receive power from one battery and either a generator (older engines) or alternator and regulator (newer engines).

The typical turboprop airplane electrical system is a 28 volt direct current (DC), which receives power from one or more batteries and a combination starter-generator. When the batteries are depleted or low, its ability to turn the compressor for engine start is greatly diminished and the possibility of engine damage due to a hot start increases. Therefore, it is essential to check the battery's condition before every engine start. The DC generators used in turboprop airplanes double as starter motors and are called "starter-generators".

The starter-generator uses electrical power to produce mechanical torque to start the engine and then uses the engine's mechanical torque to produce electrical power after the engine is running. Some of the DC power produced is changed to 28-36 volt 400 cycle alternating current (AC) power for certain avionics, lighting, and indicator synchronization functions. This is accomplished by an electrical component called an "inverter".

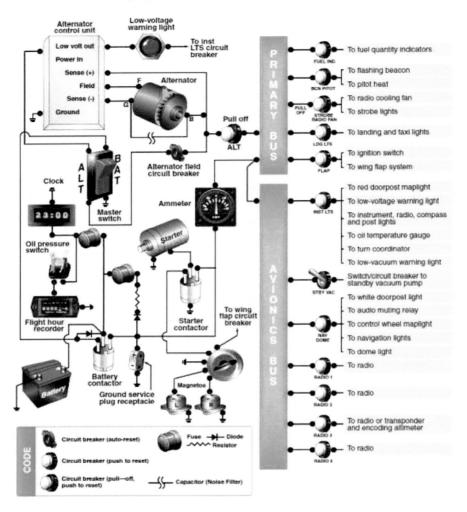

Fig 19. Example of a typical piston aircraft electrical system. (Refer also to electrical schematic diagram in your aircraft manual.)

Master power / battery switch fails to energize aircraft electrical system

1. Check fuses/circuit breakers.
2. Check all connections at battery and master solenoid contactor.
3. Check for loose wire at master switch and fuse holder/circuit breakers.
4. Master solenoid may be stuck, lightly tap solenoid with a solid object to release.
5. Bypass the master switch to energize the master solenoid contactor. Normally this is achieved by shorting out the wire that connects the master switch to the contactor to any metal part of the aircraft.
6. Turn all switches off, then bypass solenoid by shorting out the contactor terminals with a jumper cable or remove one cable from contactor and join both, the battery and buss cables, together onto one terminal. Disconnect battery once at destination and replace contactor.
7. Dead battery.

Starter switch fails to energize starter motor

1. Check fuse/circuit breakers.
2. Check all connections around starter motor and starter solenoid contactor.
3. Check for loose wire at starter switch/button and fuse holder/circuit breakers.
4. Bypass starter switch.
5. Starter solenoid contactor may be stuck, lightly tap solenoid with a solid object to release.
6. Bypass solenoid by shorting out the contactor terminals with a jumper cable.
7. Battery low. Check voltage.

Avionics circuit dead

1. Check fuses/circuit breakers.
2. Check for loose wires behind avionics switch and fuse holders/circuit breakers.

Battery not charging

If the generator or alternator lamp stays on and/or the amp gauge shows a constant discharge, the battery has not been charged.

1. Check fuses/circuit breakers.
2. Reset the alternator/generator switch. This should bring the alternator back on line again. If the aircraft is not equipped with a ALT/GEN switch, turn the master switch off and on again.
3. Check for loose or broken wires on alternator, generator or regulator unit.
4. Check for loose wires under the panel at the rear of "alternator" / "generator" switch, amp gauge or circuit breakers.
5. If the alternator or generator is driven by a drive belt, check that it is not loose or missing.

Battery not holding charge or engine difficult to start

1. Check the level of the water and top up, if necessary. Use only distilled water. In an emergency use a little boiled water that has been allowed to cool down.
2. Check that all connections on the battery are not corroded or loose.
3. Using a Hydrometer check each cell for correct gravity. If a cell is very low (in the red) after a long flight or charge, that cell may be dead and the battery will need to be replaced.

Radio and intercom problems

Always turn on avionics prior to starting engine and perform a proper radio and intercom check. Turn off the squelch and adjust the radio's volume, then reset the squelch. Whenever possible, call for a radio check. Then turn off the avionics prior to starting the engine. This will prevent a lot of frustration and sweating after start-up.

1. No intercommunication: Check if all controls on the intercom are correctly selected and adjusted. Check if all plugs are correctly inserted.

2. No reception on the radio: Check all controls on audio panel, make sure that radio and intercom are correctly selected and adjusted. Check antenna cable and antenna.

3. Radio not transmitting: Check if the Push to Talk (PTT) switch is working and if all controls on the audio panel are correctly selected and adjusted and power is on. Check circuit breaker.

4. Radio transmitting, but with very weak signal or modulation. If another station reports that your transmission is poor then don't do as I have heard an instructor telling a student pilot *"Your radio is very weak, turn up the volume on your radio"?!* Please note, if your transmission is "weak", then the only way you can improve it is as follows: Speak closer into the mike, change to another mike / set of headphones, make sure your headphones are plugged into the correct socket, check the radio's antenna or change to another radio. You cannot adjust the output power of your radio (carrier wave) or of the microphone (modulation of carrier wave) by adjusting the volume control. The output power is not user adjustable. The volume control only adjusts the level of sound in your headphones or cockpit loudspeaker.

5. Very weak reception and transmission: Your altitude may be too low. Remember that aviation radios transmit and receive between 118.0mhz and 136.0mhz. They operate in the Very High Frequency (VHF) range and transmissions are basically "line of sight", so if you are too low and have high ground between you and the other station, you may not have good transmission or reception, if any at all.

APPENDICES

Index

bush pilot training course/school

bush plane 23, 24, 62, 247

bush flying 15, 18, 23, 24, 25, 27, 28, 31, 192, 216

burns 169

C of G (Center of Gravity) 27, 30, 40, 41, 42, 49, 69, 144

camping 131, 173, 175, 182

camshaft 35, 187, 189

canyon 99, 100, 102, 104, 108, 110, 112, 114, 121, 122, 123, 124, 126

CAVOK (Cloud and Visibility OK) 140

chandelle 123

CHT (Cylinder Head Temperature) 61, 194, 202

circuit breakers 228, 230, 253, 254, 255

clothing 143, 144, 146, 147, 175, 178

clouds 98, 101, 126, 127, 128, 136, 181

combustion 186, 187, 188, 191, 198, 200, 202, 204, 205, 206, 207, 215, 216, 217, 218, 227, 228, 232, 241

communication 145, 155, 179, 250, 253

compass 97, 126, 127, 136, 145, 166, 253

compressor 205, 214, 215, 216, 221, 222, 223, 226, 227, 229, 231, 232, 233, 237, 238, 246

condenser 148, 197, 198

connecting rods 187

cooking 163, 175

crash 16, 64, 99, 146

crankshaft 131, 187, 188, 189

crosswind 75, 76, 85, 86, 137

cylinder head 61, 187, 194, 198, 202, 215

cylinder glazing 207

dead reckoning (bush pilots VOR) 136, 140

density altitude 64, 87, 91, 92, 93, 94, 97, 101, 183

detonation 36, 202, 204, 207, 208, 213, 214

distillation still 165

dogleg strips 87

downdraft 97, 98, 99, 103, 104, 105, 106, 117, 120, 122

downwind 101, 104, 132, 155, 178

downhill/uphill strips 87, 88, 91, 103, 163

drag curve 31, 46, 77, 80, 84

electrical problems 195

ELT (Emergency Locator Transmitter) 33, 145,153,155

emergency / emergencies 66, 67, 110, 120, 123, 124, 125, 126, 127, 129,
        133, 145, 148, 149, 150, 152, 153, 155, 159, 163, 166, 167, 169,
        175, 179, 213, 242, 254

engine 24, 33, 34, 35, 36, 41, 43, 44, 57, 58, 61, 62, 63, 66, 67, 69, 70, 92,
        97, 110, 111, 118, 120, 127, 129, 130, 131, 132, 143, 151, 154,
        156, 179, 186, 187, 190, 191, 192, 193, 194, 195, 196, 197, 198,
        199, 200, 201, 202, 203, 204, 206, 207, 209, 210, 212, 213, 214,
        215, 216, 217, 218, 219, 221, 222, 223, 224, 225, 226, 227, 228,
        229, 230, 232, 236, 238, 239, 240, 241, 242, 243, 244, 251, 254,
        255

engine analyser 192

engine failure 44, 66, 67, 118, 120, 129, 130, 131, 132, 192, 226, 240, 242

engine management 191

engine problems 110, 205, 230

EGT (Exhaust Gas Temperature) 192, 193, 223, 232, 241

ethanol 212, 213, 214

exciter 231, 232

PLB (Personal Locator Beacon) 145, 153, 155

POH (Pilots Operating Handbook) 30, 40, 42, 53, 62, 87, 93, 121, 122, 129, 229

point of no return 116, 117

power lines 113, 115

pre-ignition 202, 208

pre-flight 31, 183, 191, 213, 239

propeller 30, 33, 34, 35, 38, 57, 58, 62, 67, 69, 70, 88, 89, 97, 123, 139, 188, 191, 192, 198, 199, 200, 201, 211, 215, 216, 217, 218, 219, 222, 223, 224, 225, 226, 227, 228, 233, 240, 244

pitch control   192

puncture 247

pylons 114, 115, 242

QNH (Barometric Pressure) 110, 140

radio 110, 127, 145, 153, 154, 156, 157, 166, 179, 180, 225, 256

reciprocating engine 61, 62, 187, 215, 238

recovery 38, 67, 123, 128, 241

repairs 21, 191, 195, 211, 247, 248, 249, 251

river beds 49, 50, 73, 79, 163

roads 15, 27, 49, 65, 71, 86, 87, 108, 113, 123, 130

rope 51, 53, 55, 56, 57, 151, 154, 160, 175, 176, 180

rotor cloud 101

rotor shear 104

rotor wind 97, 101, 104, 120

RPM (Revolutions per minute) 33, 34, 35, 46, 62, 70, 73, 74, 75, 194, 195, 198, 200, 201, 202, 215, 216, 218, 219, 222, 223, 224, 225, 227, 230, 231, 232, 233, 234, 236, 241

VHF (Very High Frequency) 110, 145, 156

VMC (Visual Meteorological Conditions) 64, 65, 112, 126, 139

VOR (Very high frequency Omni directional Radio beacon) 136, 140

Vso (Stall Speed) 40

Vibration 234, 240, 241, 244

visibility 27, 44, 112, 118, 138, 139

visual approach

ABOUT THE AUTHOR

'CC' Milne Pocock is a commercial pilot, flight instructor, test pilot, stunt pilot and airshow performer. He has accumulated over 6000 hours of 'hands on flying' in over 50 different light to medium aircraft types including turboprops and jets. Besides that, he is also a Pyrotechnician & Special Effects Engineer, a "Jack of all trades" with a background in electronics, mechanics, aircraft airframes and engines.

54. Author's finale signature stunt seen at many airshows. Explosives are detonated by remote control from the aircraft.